MOISTURE IN MATERIALS IN RELATION TO FIRE TESTS

Presented at the

SIXTY-SEVENTH ANNUAL MEETING

AMERICAN SOCIETY FOR TESTING AND MATERIALS

Chicago, Ill., June 24, 1964

Reg. U. S. Pat. Off.

ASTM Special Technical Publication No. 385

Price $7.00; to Members $4.90

Published by the
AMERICAN SOCIETY FOR TESTING AND MATERIALS
1916 Race St., Philadelphia 3, Pa.

Printed in Baltimore, Md.
May, 1965

FOREWORD

The papers in the Symposium on Fire Tests—Moisture Influence on Material Behavior were presented on June 24, 1964, during the Sixty-seventh Annual Meeting of the Society at Chicago, Ill. Mr. A. F. Robertson chaired the symposium committee comprised of I. A. Benjamin, C. C. Carlson, R. H. Neisel, and G. W. Shorter. Mr. N. B. Hutcheon, National Research Council of Canada, presided as Chairman at the session.

CONTENTS

RELATED ASTM PUBLICATIONS

Fire Test Methods, STP 301 (1961)
Methods of Testing Building Constructions, STP 312 (1962)
Fire Test Methods, STP 344 (1962)

MOISTURE IN MATERIALS IN RELATION TO FIRE TESTS

INTRODUCTION

By A. F. Robertson[1]

It seems likely that even in the very earliest fire endurance tests, some recognition must have been made of the influence of moisture on heat transfer behavior of constructions. Because of this, precautions were suggested in ASTM Method E 119[2] to insure that most of the free water within the specimen had been evaporated prior to test. However, it was not until the mid-1950's that C. A. Menzel successfully encouraged Committee E-5 to adopt moisture conditioning requirements for constructions prior to test. Suggestions were also provided for techniques which would be useful for measuring the moisture condition of specimens.

The experience observed while trying to apply these requirements made it evident that there was a need to provide information for testing organizations and materials producers on technical problems involving moisture in materials, and in this way encourage a better understanding of the importance of considering and controlling the moisture content of materials and constructions submitted to fire test. A symposium was accordingly held in June, 1964 for this purpose.

This book includes the papers presented during this symposium. It is the hope of the committee on arrangements that the information presented will be useful by providing specific data on the manner in which moisture can influence the outcome of fire tests. However, the reader will note that a need remains for further research on moisture behavior in materials.

[1] Chief, Fire Research Section, National Bureau of Standards, Washington, D. C.
[2] Methods of Fire Tests of Building Construction and Materials (E 119), *1964 Book of ASTM Standards*, Part 14.

MOISTURE EQUILIBRIUM AND MIGRATION IN BUILDING MATERIALS

By P. J. Sereda[1] and N. B. Hutcheon[1]

Synopsis

Factors influencing the moisture content of a variety of building materials in equilibrium with their thermal and moisture environments are discussed. Reference is made to forces, potentials, energies, pore structure, surface area, and hysteresis. The usefulness of the suction concept in dealing with moisture at conditions close to saturation and of the relationship of the suction scale to relative humidity is discussed.

The second part of the paper introduces a discussion of moisture migration under isothermal steady-state conditions, and indicates the complications inherent in the nonisothermal case. We refer to some significant work by others in fields where combined heat and moisture flow is of concern.

Moisture is inevitably present as a significant factor in almost all aspects of building performance, including fire exposure. The fire scientist must therefore be interested in the moisture contents that occur in building constructions under various environmental conditions. Some of the basic aspects of moisture equilibrium and moisture migration are reviewed, keeping the interests of the fire scientist in mind.

Adsorption of Water

It is generally known that an adsorption isotherm represents the equilibrium amount of water held on the surface of a unit weight of a given material at any condition of relative humidity (RH). The theory of adsorption often is not well known and a simple discussion of the theory might give more meaning to

graphic representation and illustrate how this information can be of use to the fire technologist.

This simplified discussion on adsorption is based generally on the multimolecular theory of Brunauer et al (1).[2] It is known that water molecules are strongly attracted to the surface of most materials. Because the attraction decreases sharply when water molecules are deposited on other water molecules to build successive layers, it is reasoned that the first (monomolecular) layer will be complete before the second and subsequent layers of water molecules are deposited.

This concept allows for the determination of the point along the isotherm (usually between 0 and 30 per cent RH) when a monomolecular layer is established and the corresponding quantity of water designated as Wm is determined through

---

[1] Head, Inorganic Materials Section, and assistant director, Division of Building Research, respectively, National Research Council, Ottawa, Ont., Canada.

[2] The boldface numbers in parentheses refer to the list of references appended to this paper.

the application of the BET equation

$$\frac{P/P_0}{W(1 - P/P_0)} = \frac{1}{W m C} + \frac{(C - 1)}{W m C} (P/P_0)\ ..(1)$$

where:

W = weight of water (or any gas) adsorbed at vapor pressure P,

P_0 = saturated vapor pressure at the temperature of the sample, and

C = constant related to the heat of adsorption.

When Wm has been determined, the known value of the water molecule size may be used to arrive at a value for the total surface area of the material in question. Surface area, in this connection, refers to all the surface which water molecules can reach; for most porous

isotherm between 50 and 100 per cent RH. The relationship between the vapor pressure over the meniscus of a liquid in a capillary compared to the bulk liquid is given by the Kelvin equation

$$\ln P/P_0 = \frac{-2\gamma V}{rRT} \ldots\ldots\ldots(2)$$

where:

P = vapor pressure,

γ = surface tension,

V = molar volume of the liquid at absolute temperature, T,

R = gas constant, and

r = radius of curvature of the liquid in the capillary; thus, capillaries of the smallest radii fill at the lowest pressures.

TABLE 1—THE RELATIONSHIPS BETWEEN RELATIVE VAPOR PRESSURE, RADIUS OF CURVATURE OF MENISCUS, EQUIVALENT COLUMN OF WATER, AND pF.

P/P_0, %	Radius of Curvature, μ	Height of Column of Water		Schofield's pF
		cm	psi	
0.08	0.000147	10^7	1.42×10^5	7
49.0	0.00147	10^6	1.42×10^4	6
93.0	0.0147	10^5	1.42×10^3	5
99.3	0.147	10^4	1.42×10^2	4
99.9	1.47	10^3	1.42×10	3
99.999	147	10	1.42×10^{-1}	1
100.0	∞	0	0	...

materials this constitutes the large bounding surface for all the micro- and macropores, capillaries, or voids found inside the body of the material.

After a monomolecular layer of water is established, successive layers of water molecules are deposited as the RH is increased. Finally a stage is reached when menisci can form in the fine capillaries and the filling of the pore space is accomplished through a capillary condensation process which is governed by the relationship between the depression of the vapor pressure over the curved surface of the water and the radii of the capillaries. Roughly, this represents the region of the

Because of this relationship it is possible to relate RH to the radius of curvature of the meniscus or radius of the capillary, which in turn can be related to the theoretical height of capillary rise. Thus the potential at which a particular moisture content is held in a porous body may be expressed either in terms of RH, which directly reflects the depression of vapor pressure below that of a flat water surface, or, as was done by Schofield (2), as a negative hydraulic head. The latter, commonly referred to as suction, may be expressed in centimeters, or often more conveniently in Schofield's pF units (log of the negative head in centimeters).

Special use of this concept is made in soil technology as summarized by Penner (3). The various relationships are presented in Table 1.

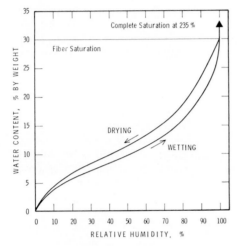

FIG. 1—Equilibrium Moisture Contents for Spruce at 20 C.

When the pores and capillaries in the material are very small (below 0.01 μ) an isotherm adequately represents the quantity of water that is held at any RH, from which the surface area and pore size are obtained. Typical isotherms are given for such materials as wood fiber (Fig. 1) and a portland cement paste (Fig. 2a). Such materials are characterized by their large surface area, usually greater than 10^6 cm²/g of material. These and other properties are given by Barkas (4) for wood, Powers and Brownyard (5) for cement, and Van Olphen (6) for clay.

Some materials may, like sand, present a pore system which consists of the interstices between relatively large and nonsorbing grains. Sand retained on 325-mesh screen, having particle diameters greater than 50μ, will have a surface area less than 10^3 cm²/g and practically all the water that will be sorbed will appear

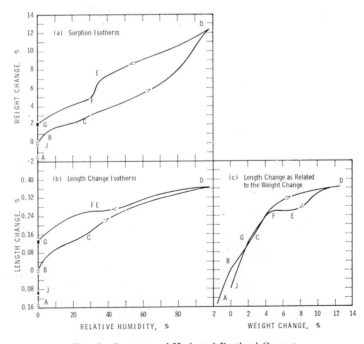

FIG. 2—Compacts of Hydrated Portland Cement.

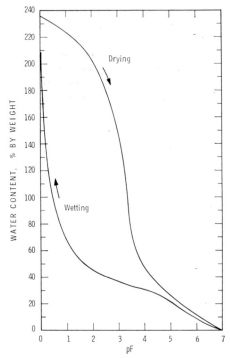

FIG. 3—Suction-Water Content Curves for Spruce at 20 C.

on the isotherm ranging between 99.9 and 100 per cent RH. Because it is not practical to control or measure humidity to the desired sensitivity in this region, the suction concept is specifically applicable to such systems. Conditioning of samples to specific levels of moisture potential can be effected on a porous plate at a potential defined by the negative head as described by Croney et al (7) for the soil system.

There are a number of mixed systems having micro- as well as macroporosity: foamed cellular concrete or natural wood are examples of such systems. The micropore part of these systems, as noted, can be represented by a normal isotherm. However, for the purpose of representing the total water to be removed before the system will be in equilibrium with RH below 99 per cent, it is best to represent it on a basis of suction (Fig. 3 for wood and Fig. 4 for foamed cellular concrete). A foamed cellular concrete consisting essentially of air bubbles in a hardened cement paste presents a micro-

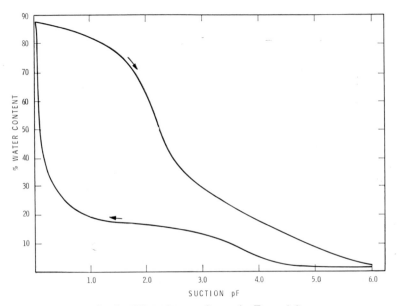

FIG. 4—Suction-Water Content Curves for Foamed Concrete.

pore system characteristic of that paste and a coarse (macro) pore system, not highly connected, represented by the enclosed air bubbles.

Isotherms or moisture content versus suction curves for most materials exhibit a hysteresis in the region from saturation to some intermediate value of moisture content. This means that two different equilibrium values of moisture content may correspond to a single condition of RH or suction, the difference being accounted for only on the basis of the direction of change (prior history). It also means that two materials or two samples of the same material at two different moisture contents, when brought together, may remain at moisture contents differing by the spread between wetting and drying curves.

These characteristics of moisture content in porous systems are of some concern in the drying of materials and measurement of moisture content. Note from Figs. 1 and 3 that wood which is completely saturated can hold more than 200 per cent water by weight (dry basis), yet the moisture content held at $pF = 4$ (99.3 per cent) is only about 40 per cent. Correspondingly, for cellular concrete (Fig. 4), the moisture content at complete saturation is 90 per cent while that at $pF = 4$ is 20 per cent or less, so that 70 per cent moisture content must be removed from a saturated sample before the RH drops below 99.3 per cent. This leads to complications in the use of RH as an index of moisture content at high moisture levels.

DIMENSIONAL CHANGES ACCOMPANYING SORPTION

There exists an imbalance of forces on the surface of a solid giving rise to surface free energy. When water is adsorbed on the surface the net result is a decrease in the free energy and will be reflected in a dimensional change of the units of solid

comprising the body. If the solid has a large surface area then the dimensional change will be correspondingly large.

The relationship of sorbed water to the dimensional change of a number of porous systems has been studied by a number of workers (8–10). These relationships are very useful when considering the mechanical properties of the porous solids. A typical relationship is given in Fig. 2c for cement paste.

The length change versus moisture content change for a given system is unique and characterizes that system. It usually has distinct regions represented by different slopes of the curve and a corresponding different response when a unit moisture content change is experienced. It follows, therefore, that moisture content gradients impose stress gradients on the body and that the magnitude of this stress depends not only on the gradient of moisture content but also on the position along the isotherm. The cracking and checking that occur when drying rapidly large sections of porous materials such as wood and concrete are examples of failure due to stress gradients as the result of moisture content gradients as discussed by Pickett (11). Wood presents a further complication since it is anisotropic with respect to drying shrinkage.

EFFECT OF TEMPERATURE CHANGES

A temperature gradient imposes a stress gradient in a material which may be superimposed, during a fire test, on stress gradients resulting from moisture content gradients. There may be a further interaction between temperature and moisture content since, as Myers (12,13) has shown, the thermal expansion of cement paste varies with moisture content. It is not possible to say, with the present state of knowledge in this field, when the effects are likely to be additive. It seems possible that under fire exposure on one side of a specimen, the drying shrinkage produced by migration of moisture from the heated face may offset in part the thermal expansion, but the situation is further complicated in the case of concrete by possible differences in both temperature and moisture responses between the cement paste and the aggregate.

Effect of Moisture on Strength

A porous, solid body having a large surface area will experience a large interaction with water as discussed earlier. This interaction usually occurs at the boundaries between units in the system where physical and chemical bonds collectively comprise the strength of the system, and has an influence upon the strength. For a nonhydrate, insoluble system, especially one of large total porosity, there usually is a decrease in strength as water is added, the greatest change being in the region from dry to monomolecular layer equivalent as shown by Dollimore and Gregg (14).

Hydrated porous systems may exhibit many unusual effects because there may be a tendency to dehydrate as the material is exposed to a low vapor pressure. This would undoubtedly have an effect on strength.

We conclude that if the strength of a porous body is affected by moisture content changes, it is quite probable that the fire endurance of such materials may be influenced by the moisture conditioning prior to test. The extent of this influence, however, cannot be predicted because the mechanisms involved are not fully understood.

Moisture Migration

The phenomenon of moisture migration is only partially understood, and the associated science has not developed an adequate set of equations describing it. Such equations as those proposed do not account adequately for all the variables involved, so that the coefficients in them are, of necessity, functions, taking into account the variables which have been disregarded. It seems necessary to suppose from what is known that some variables involving the detailed nature of the porosity, pore size distributions, interconnections between pores, and surface energy effects as they enter into the microdistribution of both thermal and moisture potentials will always be represented by empirical coefficients.

Vapor Diffusion

The equation commonly used to describe water vapor diffusion through materials is based on a form of Fick's law

$$w = -\mu \frac{dp}{dx} \quad\dots\dots\dots\dots (3)$$

where:
w = flow rate per unit area in unit time,
p = vapor pressure,
x = distance along the flow path,
and, hence:
dp/dx = vapor pressure gradient, and
μ = permeability.

Note the close parallel with Fourier's equation for heat flow. The actual transmission of vapor through a material is usually complex, so that coefficient μ is not a simple one, but is actually a function of RH and temperature and may vary along the flow path through the material in question.

Integrating Eq 3 from $x = 0$ to l and from p_1 to p_2 and rearranging, we get

$$w = \bar{\mu} \frac{(p_1 - p_2)}{l} \quad\dots\dots\dots\dots (4)$$

where:

$$\bar{\mu} = \frac{\int_{p_1}^{p_2} \mu\,dp}{p_1 - p_2}$$

and l = length of flow path, or thickness of material.

When μ is independent of p, then $\bar{\mu}$ is simply μ, but if a functional relationship exists, $\bar{\mu}$ is the average permeability coefficient applicable to the varying conditions along the flow path l, while the coefficient μ is the spot or differential permeability.

The cup or dish method is commonly used for the experimental determination of permeability coefficients (for unit thickness) or of permeance, $\bar{\mu}/l$ (for the thickness stated or implied). Various standard forms and conditions for the dish method are covered in ASTM Method C 355[3] and in ASTM E 96.[4] A discussion of the factors involved in ASTM dish methods was recently presented by Joy and Wilson (15). Application of the results obtained or building materials and their use in estimating moisture migration in building constructions can be found in the ASHRAE Guide and Data Book (16).

A mixed system of units is commonly used in building work. Vapor pressures are expressed in inches of mercury, areas in square feet, time in hours, thicknesses in inches, and weight of vapor in grains. For simplification, a permeance (for the thickness stated or implied) of 1 grain/ft²/hr/in. of mercury has been designated as 1 perm and this practice is now in common use. The corresponding unit of permeability (for unit thickness of 1 in.) is called a perm-inch.

Sheet materials highly resistant to the passage of water vapor, as used in packaging and for vapor barriers in building construction, will have permeances from 0 to 1 perm. Still air has a permeability of 120 perm-in. Most other materials have permeabilities less than that of still air, with very porous materials such as mineral wool or open fabrics approaching 120 as an upper limit.

The relationship between dry-dish results, (0 per cent one side, 50 per cent RH on the other) and wet-dish results (50 per cent RH one side, 100 per cent RH on the other) are shown for a material such as wood in Fig. 5. Note that the values $\bar{\mu}_1$ and $\bar{\mu}_2$ obtained by substituting the conditions of the respective dish tests

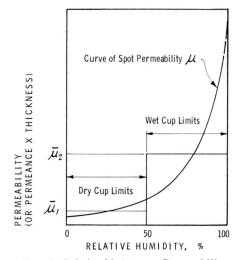

Fig. 5—Relationship between Dry- and Wet-Cup Tests and Spot Permeability for a Material such as Wood.

in Eq 4 are average values applying over the approriate ranges of RH of the two tests. Since these tests are always carried out at constant temperature there is a direct, linear relationship between vapor pressure and RH.

Moisture Migration Characteristics

The comparison of dry-dish and wet-dish values for a range of materials suggests three categories: (1) relatively impervious materials which do not show a marked functional relationship between

[3] Methods of Test for Water Vapor Transmission of Thick Materials (C 355), *1964 Book of ASTM Standards*, Part 14.

[4] Methods of Test for Water Vapor Transmission of Materials in Sheet Form (E 96), *1964 Book of ASTM Standards*, Parts 14, 15, 27, 30.

RH and permeability (dry-dish and wet-dish values the same or nearly so), (2) materials of low to medium permeability which show substantial differences between dry-dish and wet-dish values, often in the ratio of 1:2 or higher, and (3) materials of relatively high permeability which show relatively small increases in wet-dish over dry-dish values.

Many plastic films fall in the first category. It seems reasonable to suppose that they provide a kind of sieve of molecular proportions through which the water molecules must find their way. Barrer (17) has described a mechanism of activated diffusion which is related to the activation energy of the water molecules and can be identified by the temperature effect on permeability

$$\mu = \mu_0 e^{-E/RT} \ldots\ldots\ldots\ldots (5)$$

There are two possible wet-dish tests. One presents only water vapor at near-saturation to the membrane surface, since there is an air gap between the liquid water in the bottom of the cup and the test membrane above. In the other form, the dish is inverted so that liquid water comes in direct contact with the high-humidity side of the sample. For many materials, there is a marked difference in the results obtained by these two methods, the liquid contact producing higher permeabilities. Many plastic films, however, show little increase when tested in the liquid-contact condition.

Included in the third category will be those materials, such as textiles, porous papers, and solid materials, having relatively high porosity and highly connected pores in which diffusion is predominantly through air, differing from that through still air primarily to the extent that the average cross section of the air path is reduced. In working with textiles, Turl and Kennedy (18) assume that the simple diffusion theory applies and use a method of test which gives a measure of permeability in terms of an equivalent thickness of still air. In such materials in practice air flow carrying water vapor can also occur as an added mechanism. In addition, convection due to density differences whether due to temperature or to differences in water vapor content can occur. An illustration: diffusion upward through air can be markedly different from that in a downward direction.

Materials in the second category are those which generally have the capacity to sorb water and are of such a nature that this sorbed water enters into the migration process substantially. There is ample reason to suppose that the migration process is now one of a complex series—parallel flow by vapor diffusion in pores, liquid flow in small capillaries which are filled at the particular RH existing, and film flow on other surfaces of greater curvature. The gradient in vapor pressure producing flow leads also to a gradient in RH and thus in the sorbed water, since sorption is primarily related to RH.

Flow under these conditions may involve evaporation and condensation in capillaries or pores. Some thought will show that it can then no longer be strictly isothermal even when equal temperatures are maintained on bounding faces, since evaporation and condensation even on a microscale must involve energy exchanges as well; although it must be questioned whether these will always be represented exactly by the latent heat of evaporation. There is no reason with such a system to expect the simple diffusion concept to apply, and indeed it does not, as evidenced by the functional nature of the apparent permeability coefficient illustrated in a general way by Fig. 5.

It must not be supposed that all materials fall cleanly into one of the three categories described. Obviously there are many possible combinations, depending on the affinity of the surfaces presented for sorption of water, the pore sizes, and the pore-size distributions, as already discussed. The essential geometry of these systems can seldom be measured directly but is characterized in part by their sorption isotherms as mentioned, and by their moisture transmission properties.

The shape of the permeability curve of Fig. 5 for a particular material must inevitably be strongly related to the nature of its pore structure and surface energy properties. Such curves can be obtained from a series of dish tests carried out at various ranges of RH, each permeance or permeability value obtained being the average value over the particular range for which it was obtained (19).

Unfortunately few such curves are available since they are time consuming to obtain, even when restricted to one temperature. Further work can produce a series of such curves for different temperatures, indicating further the effects of temperature, but these are still not applicable except on a crude approximation basis to the general case, in which both vapor pressure and temperature gradients are imposed.

Combined Diffusion and Capillary Flow

Some workers, notably Krischer, recognized as early as 1940 the essential nature of the moisture migration mechanisms outlined. An extensive bibliography covering European work is contained in a more recent paper by Krischer et al (20). Krischer proposes an equation of the form $G = G_K + G_D$ in which G_K represents the contribution of capillary movement and G_D, vapor diffusion. Johansson (21) proposed a similar equation which for present purposes may be expressed

$$w = -\mu \frac{dp}{dx} - \mu' \frac{dc}{dx} \dots \dots (6)$$

The second part, added to that given as Eq 3, shows a contributory mechanism dependent upon a concentration gradient, or moisture content gradient, dc/dx, and another coefficient μ'. It may now be supposed that the permeability curve of

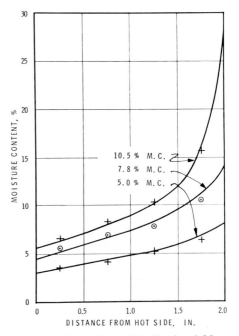

Fig. 6—Comparison of Predicted and Measured Moisture Distributions in Moist Sawdust Subjected to a Temperature Gradient.

Fig. 5 represents a base portion having the characteristics of diffusion, and that the increase with increasing humidity may be attributed to moisture content. Under a nominal isothermal flow condition, both vapor pressure and moisture content gradients will be negative in the direction of flow, so that, according to Eq 6, both contribute to the moisture migration, accounting for the increase in permeability at higher RH.

Some interesting experimental evi-

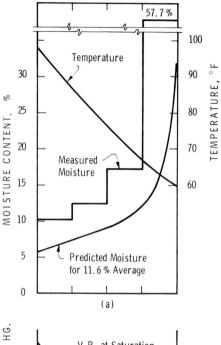

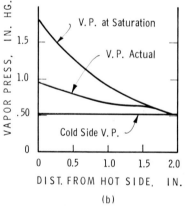

FIG. 7—Final Conditions Throughout a Closed Cell Containing Moist Sawdust Subjected to a Temperature Gradient.

dence is provided by the work of Paxton and Hutcheon (22). The material used was moist sawdust, subjected to a temperature gradient in a closed system so that the net flow across each transverse plane was zero. It was found that the steady-state distributions of moisture could be predicted from the equilibrium

moisture isotherms for wood, on the assumption of a constant vapor pressure throughout, so long as the amount of moisture present was not greatly in excess of that required to produce saturation at the cold face (Fig. 6). When the moisture content was markedly increased, however, the excess moisture did not remain at the cold face, but at all points produced moisture contents higher than those consistent with a constant vapor pressure equivalent to saturation at the cold face (Fig. 7). A curve of actual vapor pressure was then drawn for the values of moisture content actually measured for the four sampling zones (Fig. 7b using equilibrium moisture isotherm data as before) and a vapor pressure gradient was shown to exist.

Further consideration of any such closed system forces one to the conclusion that no net flow takes place. If the equation combines two mechanisms (Eq 6) the contribution of one part must exactly oppose the other at all points along the flow path. Then, if there is a moisture content gradient which can produce flow there must also be an opposing vapor pressure gradient.

At this stage it can be recognized without further argument, that, for a given imposed vapor pressure gradient, the temperature gradient may be varied almost independently, giving rise to corresponding variations in RH and thus in equilibrium moisture content at various points along a flow path. There is thus every reason to believe that a whole stream of values for the permeability coefficient of Eq 3 may be found, depending on the particular combinations of temperature gradients with any given vapor gradient. If this is so, one must accept some such form of flow equation as Eq 6, with its attendant difficulties in relating dc/dx to dp/dx and RH. Thus, both heat flow and moisture flow become involved.

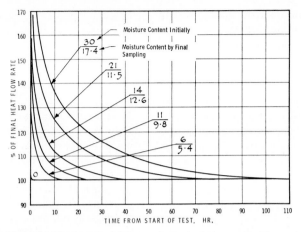

FIG. 8—Variation in Heat Flow with Time in Moist Sawdust Subjected to a Sudden Change in Temperature on One Face.

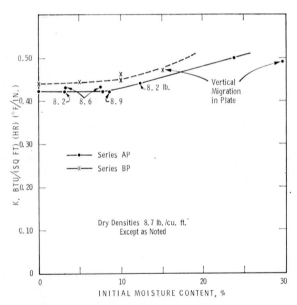

FIG. 9—Variation in Measured Conductivity Under Steady-State Conditions for Various Moisture Contents in Moist Sawdust.

COMBINED HEAT AND MOISTURE FLOW

The difficulty involved in the lack of any adequate mathematical expression to describe moisture migration is far more serious than any of the problems mentioned. Not only is there a serious limit on the prediction of moisture migration, but the corresponding capability to predict heat flow in moist materials is similarly restricted. The two flow mechanisms of heat and moisture are so thoroughly interrelated, one must be considered with the other; it is always appropriate to think of them together as combined heat and moisture flow.

It has long been recognized that the effect of moisture under a temperature gradient is generally to increase the rate of heat flow compared to that in dry material under the same temperature gradient. It is unwise to assume, however, that new conductivities corresponding to various moisture contents can be assigned for use in conduction theory, except in the case of a completely saturated material, since the added energy transfer may be largely associated with vapor flow rather than with a particular level of moisture content. An example of this may be drawn from work previously described (22), as in Figs. 8 and 9. Figure 8 shows the rate of heat flow in moist sawdust at various times after an abrupt change in temperature from a condition of uniform moisture and temperature at 60 deg throughout, to 100 F on one face. These flow rates for the various moisture contents are expressed as percentages of the final steady-state rate. The final rates are shown in Fig. 9 where we see that once moisture redistribution took place, the resulting thermal conductivity was not affected until the average moisture content was increased about $7\frac{1}{2}$ per cent. Beyond that point an increase of about 1 per cent for each per cent increase in moisture content (dry basis) took place. These results are interesting in comparison with those of Cammerer (23), who many years ago proposed two sets of wet conductivities, one for organic and one for inorganic materials. For the former he proposed a value of $1\frac{1}{4}$ per cent for 1 per cent increase in moisture on a dry weight basis and for the latter, a series of values based on moisture content by volume. That is, 1 per cent by volume = 0.625 lb/ft³, as follows:

Moisture Content, %	Increase in Conductivity, %
1	32
2	48
5	75
10	108
20	144

Cammerer's values were developed largely from the experimental work of others. These, or similar values, have been widely used in Europe for want of a more rational method of calculating heat losses through damp building constructions. Clearly, they relate to some arbitrarily selected moisture gradient conditions and cannot rationally account for other gradient conditions which might exist.

MOISTURE MIGRATION IN VARIOUS FIELDS

This discussion has referred to work selected to illustrate the nature of the mechanisms involved. Workers in a number of fields have been concerned with moisture migration, and we will review briefly.

The work of soil scientists concerned with the moisture available to growing crops has been very extensive and outstanding. Being mainly concerned with relatively high levels of moisture content, they have generally worked with the suction concept and have used the negative hydraulic head as the measure of moisture potential rather than vapor pressure. This has several advantages, one being that differences in potential head due to elevation can be taken into account readily. The corresponding permeability coefficients differ from those of the simple vapor diffusion equation by the relationship between RH (or vapor pressure at constant temperature) and negative hydraulic head, or suction. Temperature gradients were not usually accounted for in earlier work. Discussions can be found in any good text on soil physics. Croney et al (24) used similar approaches in predicting the migration of moisture in soils under roads. Philip (25), concerned with agricultural applications, has done extensive work on moisture migration in soils and has taken up the combined heat and moisture flow problem. Taylor (26) has also been concerned with the general case.

Chemical engineers concerned with industrial drying processes have been involved with moisture migration, and another paper in this book reviews developments in this field.

In buildings work, there has been great interest, particularly in Europe, in the effects of moisture upon heat transmission through masonry building constructions. The work of Krischer, Cammerer, and others has already been referred to. In North American building, the interest in theories of moisture migration has developed very little beyond the use of membranes to control vapor diffusion in structures (16). Some work has been carried out on the effect of moisture on heat transmission, but no generally acceptable basis has been established for the estimation of moisture effects.

Conclusion

The fire scientist is hampered, as are others concerned with problems of drying, prediction of moisture transfer, and heat transfer in moist materials, by the present limitations in knowledge of combined heat and moisture flow. He has drying problems in the conditioning of his specimens. He is presented, under fire exposure conditions, with high temperature, high gradient, highly transient situations inevitably involving both heat and moisture, which he cannot ignore. He can only hope that at the exaggerated conditions involved in fire exposures, some approximations may be possible which will allow him to predict—with acceptable accuracy for limited purposes —the moisture effects with which he is concerned.

References

(1) S. Brunauer, *Adsorption of Gases and Vapours*, Princeton University Press, Princeton, N. J., 1943.

(2) R. K. Schofield, "The pF of Water in the Soil," *Transactions*, Third International Congress of Soil Science, Vol. 2, 1935, pp. 37–48.

(3) E. Penner, "Suction and its Use as a Measure of Moisture Contents and Potentials in Porous Materials," *Proceedings*, International Symposium on Humidity and Moisture (in press).

(4) W. W. Barkas, "The Swelling of Wood under Stress—A Discussion of Its Hygroscopic, Elastic, and Plastic Properties," Her Majesty's Stationery Office, Department of Scientific and Industrial Research—Forest Products Research, London, 1949.

(5) T. C. Powers and T. L. Brownyard, "Studies of the Physical Properties of Hardened Portland Cement Paste," *Bulletin 22*, Portland Cement Assn., Chicago, Ill., March, 1948.

(6) H. Van Olphen, *An Introduction to Clay Colloid Chemistry*, Interscience Publishers, Inc., New York, N. Y.-London, 1963.

(7) D. Croney, J. D. Coleman, and P. M. Bridge, "The Suction of Moisture Held in Soil and other Porous Materials," *Road Research Technical Paper 24*, Department of Scientific and Industrial Research, Road Research Laboratory, 1952.

(8) R. F. Feldman and P. J. Sereda, "Moisture Content, Its Significance and Interaction in a Porous Body," *Proceedings*, International Symposium on Humidity and Moisture (in press).

(9) C. H. Amberg and R. McIntosh, "A Study of Adsorption Hysteresis by Means of

Length Changes of a Rod of Porous Glass," *Canadian Journal of Chemistry*, Vol. 30, 1952, p. 1012.

(10) D. H. Bangham and F. A. B. Maggs, "The Strength and Elastic Constants of Coals in Relation to their Ultra-Fine Structure," *Proceedings*, Conference on the Ultrafine Structure of Coals and Cokes, British Coal Utilization Research Assn., 1944, p. 118.

(11) G. Pickett, "Shrinkage Stresses in Concrete," *Proceedings*, American Concrete Inst., Vol. 42, 1946, pp. 165–204; 361–398.

(12) S. L. Myers, "Thermal Expansion Characteristics of Hardened Cement Paste and of Concrete," *Proceedings*, Highway Research Board, Vol. 30, 1950, pp. 193–203.

(13) S. L. Myers, "How Temperatures and Moisture Changes May Affect the Durability of Concrete," *Rock Products*, Vol. 54, 1951, pp. 153–157; 178.

(14) D. Dollimore and S. J. Gregg, "The Strength of Brittle Solids," *Research*, Vol. 11, 1958, pp. 180–184.

(15) F. A. Joy and A. G. Wilson, "Standardization of the Dish Method for Measuring Water Vapor Transmission," *Proceedings*, International Symposium on Humidity and Moisture (in press).

(16) *Guide and Data Book*, American Society of Heating, Refrigeration and Air-Conditioning Engineers, Vol. 1, Chap. 6, "Fundamentals and Equipment," New York, N. Y., 1963.

(17) R. M. Barrer, *Diffusion in and through Solids*, Cambridge, The University Press, London, 1951.

(18) L. H. Turl and J. E. Kennedy, "Method for the Measurement of the Resistance to Water Vapor Diffusion of Clothing Materials," *Proceedings*, International Symposium on Humidity and Moisture (in press).

(19) S. C. Chang and N. B. Hutcheon, "Dependence of Water Vapor Permeability on Temperature and Humidity," *Transactions*, American Society of Heating and Air-Conditioning Engineers, Vol. 62, 1956, pp. 437–450.

(20) O. Krischer, W. Wissman, and W. Kast, "Feuchtigkeitsein-wirkungen auf Baustoffe aus der Umgebenden Luft," *Gesundheits-Ingenieur*, Vol. 79, No. 5, 1958, pp. 129–148 (available in translation as Library Communication 855, Building Research Station, Garston, Department of Scientific and Industrial Research, London).

(21) C. H. Johansson, "Fuktgenomgang och Fuktfördelning; Byggnads - Material," (Moisture Transmission and Moisture Distribution in Building Materials), *Tid. Värme* (Ventilations) *Sanitetskek*, Vol. 19, 1948, p. 67 (available as National Research Council Technical Translation 189).

(22) J. A. Paxton and N. B. Hutcheon, "Moisture Migration in a Closed Guarded Hot Plate," *Transactions*, American Society of Heating and Ventilating Engineers, Vol. 58, 1952, pp. 301–320.

(23) J. S. Cammerer, "Der Einfluss der Feuchtigkeit auf den Wärmeschutz von Bau— und Dämmstoffen nach den internationalen Schrifttum," (The Effect of Moisture on Heat Transmission through Building and Insulating Materials), *Wärme—u. Kalt tech*, Vol. 41, No. 9, 1939, pp. 126–135 (available as National Research Council Technical Translation 317).

(24) D. Croney, J. D. Coleman, and P. M. Black, "Movement and Distribution of Water in Soil in Relation to Highway Design and Performance," *Special Report 40*, Highway Research Board, 1958, pp. 226–252.

(25) J. R. Philip and D. A. DeVries, "Moisture Movement in Porous Materials Under Temperature Gradients," *Transactions*, American Geophysical Union, Vol. 38, 1957, pp. 222–232.

(26) S. A. Taylor and L. Cavazza, "The Movement of Soil Moisture in Response to Temperature Gradients," *Proceedings*, Soil Science Society of America, Vol. 18, 1954, pp. 351–358.

DISCUSSION

M. S. Abrams[1] and C. C. Carlson[1]—Perhaps concrete ranks with the most complex of building materials because its behavior regarding moisture migration is affected by so many variables. As is well known, the water-cement ratio and the duration of moist curing affect the permeability of the hardened paste. Aggregate type and aggregate pore structure also have important influences on the retention of moisture in, and rate of moisture movement through, sections. We have found that in natural drying for the fire test (drying at normal temperatures and humidities) of concretes containing expanded shale aggregates, the required drying time may be twice that for concretes containing natural sand and gravel aggregates, even though the cement content and initial moist curing are identical. On the other hand, some lightweight aggregate types such as those produced by a sintering or quenching process may produce concretes that will lose water more rapidly than some normal weight concretes by virtue of the coarser and interconnected pore structure of the aggregate particles.

Perhaps the most interesting fact of regarding the movement of moisture through concrete is that it moves primarily in a condensed state rather than in the vapor phase. Under such conditions the driving force that moves the moisture is not proportional to the vapor pressure differential between the at-

mosphere and the concrete, but to the logarithm of the ratio of these pressures. Thus, for concrete at a given equilibrium vapor pressure, a pressure of many atmospheres is required to produce a given moving force when the water migrates in the adsorbed or condensed state. Large driving forces are obviously not generated under normal drying conditions so the migration of moisture in mature concrete is therefore often a slow process.

We agree with the authors that RH does not uniquely define the moisture content of concrete. RH is useful in evaluating the heat transmission properties of concrete which has been naturally conditioned for the fire test. However, it has, as we have found, some serious drawbacks as an indicator of fire endurance when drying is accelerated by heated air.

P. J. Sereda and N. B. Hutcheon (authors)—We agree that migration of moisture in concrete is a slow process and in this regard we will amplify the above remarks. When a vapor pressure gradient exists it will result in vapor diffusion as well as flow of moisture in the condensed state. For the vapor diffusion process the rate can be expressed as the product of the coefficient μ and the vapor pressure difference; the coefficient usually being a function of the moisture and temperature conditions as well as of the material. Because the capillaries in concrete are very small much of the flow of moisture can occur in the condensed state and may be represented by the product of an appropriate coefficient

[1] Senior research engineer and manager, respectively, Fire Research Laboratory, Research and Development Laboratories, Portland Cement Assn., Skokie, Ill.

and the suction gradient. The suction gradient is the gradient in the negative head, which can be very large for small gradients of vapor pressure; the potential difference between two sections of concrete, one at equilibrium with 50 per cent RH and another at equilibrium with 99.99 per cent RH will be 10^4 cm of water. The rate of flow of water resulting from such a high potential difference, however, is relatively small because the corresponding permeability coefficient is small.

D. HANSEN[2]—Equation 3 is labeled "a form of Fick's law." This is not absolutely true. While Fick's law of diffusion, under special conditions, may be put in the form of Eq 3, neither these conditions, nor the law itself, applies to the present situation of diffusion in a porous medium. However, Eq 3 is commonly used for describing diffusion in porous media, and I have no objection to its application in this case.

MR. SEREDA AND MR. HUTCHEON— We do not wish to dispute the point made by Professor Hansen. In referring to a form of Fick's law we were following the lead of J. D. Babbitt, who did much to establish the diffusion approach to the migration of moisture through building materials.[3]

[2] Assistant professor of chemical engineering, Rensselaer Polytechnic Inst., Troy, N. Y.

[3] "The Diffusion of Water Vapour Through Various Building Materials," *Canadian Journal of Research*, Vol. 17, Section A, 1939, pp. 15–32.

THE DRYING PROCESS

By David Hansen[1]

Synopsis

Recent research has yielded a qualitatively comprehensive picture of the drying process which differs from the classical theory in many details but confirms the general features of the constant-rate period and falling-rate period. Drying experiments including continuous precise measurements of drying rates, moisture distribution, and temperature distribution have been reported. The influence of the nature of the solid on the falling-rate period has been clarified. The existence of a characteristic temperature for the falling-rate period has been observed. Because of its correspondence to the wet-bulb temperature of the constant-rate period, this characteristic temperature has been named the pseudo-wet-bulb temperature. The falling-rate period is not yet amenable to general quantitative analysis although some progress has been made.

Further development of drying theory will depend on gaining a better understanding of the mechanisms of simultaneous heat and mass transfer in porous materials. Work on this subject is proceeding, but these mechanisms, and the material properties controlling them, are not sufficiently well defined at present to permit their incorporation into quantitative drying theory.

Symbols

C . . . . Heat capacity of liquid, Btu lb^{-1} (deg F)$^{-1}$.

h . . . . Heat transfer coefficient Btu hr^{-1} ft^{-2} deg F^{-1}.

k_g . . . . Mass transfer coefficient, lb ft^{-2} hr^{-1} (psi)$^{-1}$.

p_a . . . . Partial pressure of vapor in air stream, psi.

p_s . . . . Vapor pressure at evaporation surface temperature, psi.

p_{wb} . . . . Vapor pressure at wet-bulb temperature, psi.

q . . . . Heat flux, Btu ft^{-2}.

t_a . . . . Air temperature, deg F.

t_s . . . . Temperature of evaporation surface, deg F.

w . . . . Liquid evaporated, lb ft^{-2}.

λ . . . . Latent heat of vaporization, Btu lb^{-1}.

θ . . . . Time, hr.

In the 1930's, a number of drying studies were reported (1,2,3).[2] The now classical description of drying in terms of a constant-rate period and a falling-rate period developed from this work. In 1949, Pearse et al (4) published a refined interpretation of drying which is still applicable. More recent studies of the drying process have not yielded a new interpretation, but have been directed either at a detailed analysis of specific processes or at further refinement of the classical description. Consequently,

[1] Assistant professor, Department of Chemical Engineering, Rensselaer Polytechnic Inst., Troy, N. Y.

[2] The boldface numbers in parentheses refer to the list of references appended to this paper.

a comprehensive, qualitative description of drying is now possible, but quantitative analysis, particularly of the falling-rate period, is crude and incomplete. To overcome this deficiency a better understanding of heat and mass transport in porous media is needed.

Classical Drying Theory:

Suppose that a wet porous material is placed in an air stream held at constant temperature, velocity, and humidity. Water will evaporate from the surface into the air stream and will be replaced by liquid drawn from the interior. This

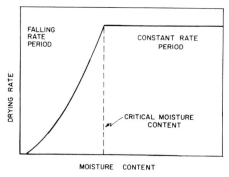

FALLING RATE PERIOD

CONSTANT RATE PERIOD

DRYING RATE

CRITICAL MOISTURE CONTENT

MOISTURE CONTENT

FIG. 1—Classical Drying-Rate Curve.

flow occurs because of a capillary pressure potential created as soon as the surface liquid retreats into the pore structure creating curved surfaces. The energy for continued evaporation is supplied by transfer from the air stream to the wet body. Quantitatively, the classical constant-rate period is described by the following equations:

For the heat flux from air to wet solid

$$\frac{dq}{d\theta} = h(t_a - t_s)\ldots\ldots\ldots(1)$$

For the rate of evaporation into the air stream

$$\frac{dw}{d\theta} = k_g(p_s - p_a)\ldots\ldots\ldots(2)$$

At steady state, the heat imput equals the heat carried out by the evaporating liquid

$$\frac{dq}{d\theta} = [\lambda + C(t_a - t_s)]\frac{dw}{d\theta}\ldots\ldots(3)$$

$$h(t_a - t_s) = [\lambda + C(t_a - t_s)]k_g(p_s - p_a)\ldots(4)$$

Since h and k_g are directly functions of the air stream conditions, t_s is uniquely determined from external conditions, and is, in fact, the well known wet-bulb temperature. The drying rate is then

$$\frac{dw}{d\theta} = k_g(p_{wb} - p_a)\ldots\ldots\ldots(5)$$

Equation 5 contains only factors relating to the air stream, and is independent of the material (solid) being dried. The time, or moisture content range, through which the drying rate is given by Eq 5 is called the constant-rate period.

When the liquid content of the material drops to a level where capillary flow to the surface can no longer be maintained at a rate equal to the drying rate given by Eq 5 the actual drying rate falls off. The liquid content at which this occurs is termed the critical moisure content. The picture of air drying according to the classical analysis is summarized by Fig. 1.

The falling-rate period, or the time or moisture content range through which the drying rate falls off rapidly, presents a substantially more complex problem than the constant-rate period. First, the critical moisture content must be determined. Often, this parameter is assumed to be a constant of the material being dried, independent of the drying conditions. Actually, it is a complex, imprecise, and as yet unpredictable function of the material and the drying conditions. To complete the analysis, a description of the decline in drying rate with moisture content from the critical moisture content to complete dryness is needed. This description, in turn, cannot be made general as it depends on the nature of the material as well as the external drying conditions. For purposes of calculation, the falling-rate curve is often approximated by a simple mathematical form. However, these procedures are arbitrary and drying calculations based on them can be validated only by comparison with actual drying data.

The classical theory of drying applies exactly only to the air drying at constant what from the one given above, and the terms constant-rate period and falling-rate period are applied loosely to refer, respectively, to the moisture content range where the external conditions are controlling, and that where the material properties are controlling.

The Pseudo-Wet-Bulb Temperature:

The simplest picture of air drying during the falling-rate period is that of a receding plane of vaporization with

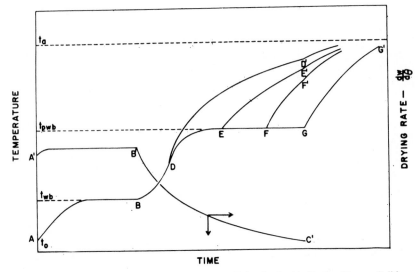

FIG. 2—General Drying Rate—Temperature Behavior in Air Drying Porous Solids.

conditions of some hypothetical, ideal material. While it may be inexact as applied to real drying situations, the general features of the classical theory have been validated experimentally many times for many different materials. That is, a constant, or nearly constant, rate period is observed which is followed by a relatively sharp falloff at some critical moisture content. In other than air drying at constant conditions (radiant heat drying, conduction drying, etc.) a constant-rate period may or may not occur. In these cases the analysis according to the classical theory differs somedry material above and wet material below. Nissan et al (5,6) described this picture of drying in the falling-rate period quantitatively with equations derived from heat and mass balances at the evaporation surface. From this analysis, they concluded that just as a body tends to the wet-bulb temperature during the constant-rate period it tends to another characteristic temperature during the falling-rate period. This they termed the pseudo-wet-bulb temperature. This analysis of the falling-rate period is subject to the same weaknesses as the classical analysis of the constant-rate period.

However, its general features have also been experimentally validated. That is, during the falling-rate period the moisture distribution in many materials is marked by a relatively sharp demarcation between wet material and dry material, and a predictable pseudo-wet-bulb temperature is observed. The general picture of temperature and drying rate behavior from Nissan's analysis for convection air drying is as shown in Fig. 2.

and the air temperature. Each of these is predictable *a priori* from a knowledge of drying conditions. To a first approximation they do not depend on the nature of the solid being dried. However, the rise, or approach, to each of these characteristic temperatures is less predictable with respect to the moisture content at which it occurs and how rapidly it takes place. This behavior is a function not only of the drying conditions but of the

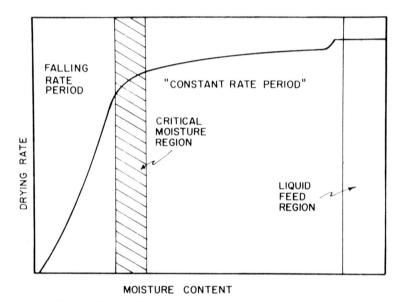

FIG. 3—General Drying-Rate Curve in Convection Air Drying.

The temperature first rises (or falls if it was initially above the wet-bulb temperature) to the wet-bulb value, t_{wb}, holding constant until the end of the constant-rate period is reached at B. The temperature then rises along $BDEF$ to a higher value, t_{pwb}. However, as successive layers achieve total dryness, they tend to the air temperature, t_a, along curves D-D', E-E', F-F', etc.

The temperature history of a material during drying contains three plateaus corresponding to the wet-bulb temperature, the pseudo-wet-bulb temperature,

heat and mass transfer mechanisms operating within the body being dried. The lack of understanding of these mechanisms prevents the immediate adaptation of Nissan's analysis to provide a general and complete description of temperatures and drying rates in the falling-rate period.

Refinement of Classical Drying Theory:

In recent years the problem of refining the classical drying analysis has been attacked both theoretically and experimentally. Advances in boundary layer theory permit more rigorous treatment of heat and mass transfer at the surfaces of material during drying. Luikov (7,8) has considered the influence of mass transfer on the boundary layer at the surface of a drying material. He concluded that droplets can disengage from the surface, become trapped in the boundary layer, and evaporate there. Quantitatively, Luikov claims these effects can be incorporated into the determination of heat and mass transfer coefficients by including a dimensionless number which is the difference between air temperature and wet-bulb temperature divided by air temperature.

Perhaps even more important than boundary layer effects are the changes in the liquid evaporation surface. During the constant-rate period the picture from the classical analysis is a flat liquid surface maintained by capillary flow. Actually, in order to maintain capillary flow, the liquid must recede at least slightly from the surface to form curved liquid surfaces. Without these curved liquid surfaces there is no potential for capillary liquid flow. When the liquid recedes, the resistance to heat and mass transfer between wet solid and the air stream is increased. Bartlett (9) reported some precise experimental measurements of drying rates which point up the importance of this effect. This result can be represented by a drying-rate curve of the shape shown in Fig. 3.

Three general features of the drying-rate data obtained by Bartlett are particularly significant. One, if the porous solid was supplied with liquid from a reservoir such that it was kept 100 per cent liquid saturated and did not need to develop a capillary potential to maintain a wet surface, then a constant-drying or evaporation rate was observed in agreement with the classical drying analysis. However, when the liquid supply was disconnected, a sharp drop

in drying rate would follow almost immediately. Two, as drying progressed, the drying rate decreased gradually. There was no constant-rate period. Three, there was no sharp, critical moisture content but, rather, the drying rate showed a change to more rapid decrease over a critical moisture range. The interpretation of these observations is as follows. While the liquid reservoir was connected a flat liquid surface was maintained, exposed to the air stream. When the reservoir was cut off the liquid surface receded slightly to form curved surfaces which maintained capillary flow

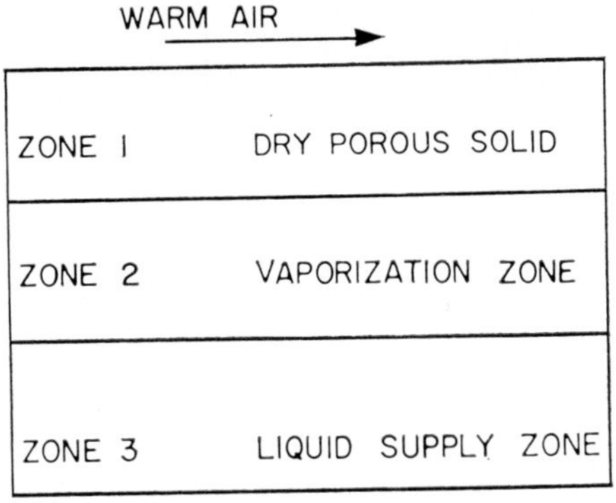

WARM AIR →

FIG. 4—Zones Within Porous Solid During Drying in Falling-Rate Period.

of liquid, but caused a drop in drying rate. As drying proceeded, the liquid surface would recede further as necessary to provide the capillary force for sustaining liquid flow. Hence, a gradual decline in drying rate was observed. At some point in the drying process, the liquid content becomes too low to maintain an effective continuous network for liquid flow. This is the critical moisture content which shows up in Bartlett's results as a finite range rather than a sharp point. Unfortunately this parameter remains largely unpredictable although Bartlett does give some insight on its prediction for certain classes of materials.

The experimental work of Adams (10)

confirmed and amplified the results of Bartlett. Using an X ray absorption technique, Adams was able to monitor liquid distribution during a drying experiment. Whereas Bartlett's results demonstrate the shortcomings of certain details of the classical drying analysis, Adams' results support the general features of the classical analysis. Adams' measurements of liquid distribution

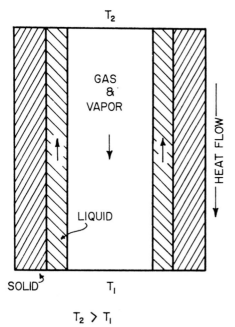

T_2

GAS
&
VAPOR

HEAT FLOW

LIQUID

SOLID T_1

$T_2 > T_1$

FIG. 5—Idealized Capillary with Wetted Walls in Temperature Field.

clearly show that initially all evaporation occurs at or very near the surface, with liquid migrating from the interior to keep the surface wet. In the falling-rate period Adams showed that, rather than evaporation from an interior plane as Nissan and his earlier co-workers postulated, there was evaporation from a zone of significant thickness. Adams' picture of drying in its later stages has the material divided into three zones, shown schematically in Fig. 4. Zone 1 is

the layer of completely dry material below which are Zone 2 (vaporization) and Zone 3 which contains sufficient liquid to supply Zone 2 by capillary flow. Hence, the picture of the air-drying process obtained by Adams closely parallels the classical picture. Initially there is evaporation at the surface with liquid flow from the interior. At the critical moisture content this flow cannot be maintained at a sufficient rate, and evaporation begins to extend further inward. As the evaporation extends deeper the surface becomes completely dry and the three zones are established. As drying continues still further Zone 1 grows while Zone 3 gradually disappears, as does Zone 2 when the material is completely dry.

Adams' observations were made on air drying of a bed of particulate solids. However, the same general picture was obtained by Cowan (11) from observations of moisture distribution and temperatures in hot surface drying of fibrous sheets. The details are different, but these differences can be directly related to the boundary conditions. That is, with heat supplied at a closed surface, Cowan observed migration of liquid to this surface which was evaporated and diffused back through the structure to the open surface. Either evaporation or condensation occurred within the bulk of the material depending on the temperature gradients existing at the particular stage of drying. When the moisture content fell to a value too low to maintain continuity of flow to the hot surface, all the energy for drying had to be conducted to the interior, and drying rates fell off rapidly. In hot surface drying the moisture is removed most readily from the hot surface and the open surface; and more slowly from the middle regions. It is this characteristic of both air drying and hot surface drying that causes the drying rate to become very small in the last stages of drying. The remaining moisture at these stages is concentrated in the interior, and hence the heat for evaporation must traverse the resistance of the covering of dry material and the vapor must diffuse through this barrier to the surface.

The biggest obstacle is the lack of understanding the mechanisms of heat and mass transfer in the porous media which control drying behavior in the falling-rate period. This is a complex problem, formulated only recently by Krischer (12).

An approximation of the problem:

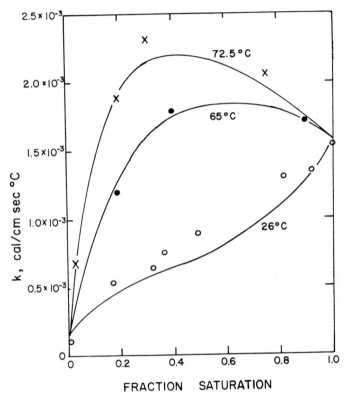

FIG 6—Heat Transfer in Woven Fiberglass-Water-Air System as a Function of Liquid Content and Temperature.

Heat and Mass Transfer in Porous Media:

The results of Bartlett, Adams, Cowan, and earlier workers have provided a comprehensive, qualitative picture of the drying process. Preparing a quantitative analysis which would permit accurate *a priori* prediction of drying behavior from a knowledge of characteristics of the solid, the liquid, and external conditions is not yet possible.

Imagine a capillary with its walls wetted by a volatile liquid and with a temperature gradient imposed along its length as in Fig. 5. The imposed temperature gradient will create a vapor pressure gradient causing diffusion of vapor from hot to cooler regions. Consequently, there will be evaporation occurring in hotter, and corresponding condensation in cooler regions. In any actual porous structure the situation will not be as simple as that in Fig. 5, but the result will be similar. The diffusion of vapor has two effects: (1) It transports material, and (2) It transports energy (the latent heat of evaporation). In a steady-state situation the diffusion would be counteracted by a countercurrent liquid flow maintained by the capillary forces on the liquid and the net result would be only the transport of the latent heat of vaporization. The magnitude of this energy transport is demonstrated by the graph in Fig. 6 from data of Nissan et al (13). In this graph the effective thermal conductivity (energy transferred per unit temperature gradient) is plotted against fraction saturation (fraction of pore space occupied by liquid). Two features stand out: the effect of liquid content and the temperature sensitivity. The latter is due to vapor pressure sensitivity of the evaporation-diffusion-concentration mechanism described above. At 26 C the vapor pressure is low, this mechanism is ineffective, and the effective thermal conductivity increases gradually with liquid content reflecting the higher thermal conductivity of liquid water compared to air and water vapor. At 65 C and 72.5 C, however, this mechanism is very active. As the liquid content increases above zero saturation the heat transfer rate rises rapidly to levels three or four times greater than observed at 26 C. A maximum is reached between 30 and 50 per cent saturation. Beyond this point, liquid occupies much of the pore space and the effective volume for diffusion is less.

Quantitative prediction or analysis of results like those in Fig. 6 is not yet possible. Krischer and Esdorn (12) have developed an essentially empirical method of analyzing data. However, a better fundamental understanding of the simultaneous heat and mass transfer mechanisms and the coupling between

them will be necessary before considerations of them can be incorporated into drying theory. This problem is being studied and a recent book by Luikov and Mikhailov (14) treats some aspects of the problem by application of the formalisms of nonequilibrium thermodynamics.

Hot Surface, Dielectric, and Radiant Heat Drying:

When heat is supplied to the material by agencies other than a heated air stream the analysis of drying behavior must include considerations of these additional factors. In general this can be done in a straightforward way for the constant-rate period but is hampered by the same problems as air drying analysis when the falling-rate period is considered.

Hot surface drying has been studied in considerable detail, particularly the drying of sheet materials (11,15,16). Analysis of this type of drying is strongly dependent on knowledge of the heat transfer behavior of the solid. Likewise, analysis of dielectric and radiant heat drying requires consideration not only of the heat transfer characteristics of the solid, but the dielectric or radiant absorption properties of the solid as well. In these types of drying the temperature is not necessarily limited to the surrounding or air temperature, but can reach much higher levels. In one study of radiant heat drying, Hansen (17) presents data and an analysis which demonstrate the sensitivity of drying rate to the relative reflection and absorption of radiant energy at the surface. It is shown that these characteristics are moisture-content and wave-length sensitive.

Conclusions:

The classical analysis of drying in terms of a constant-rate period and a falling-rate period is valid in its general features. When dealing with other than constant conditions in air drying, the term, constant-rate period, should be interpreted as referring to that part of the drying process where moisture content is relatively high and drying behavior can be analyzed or predicted from considerations of external conditions for heat and mass transfer. Likewise, the term, falling-rate period, should be interpreted as referring to that part of the drying process where the moisture content is relatively low and the conditions and behavior within the porous solid control drying.

The primary shortcoming of classical drying theory is its inability to deal quantitatively with the falling-rate period or to predict the critical moisture content. Recent experimental research has provided a comprehensive picture of the details of the drying process and a better understanding of the underlying mechanisms of drying. Sufficient progress has not been made, however, to permit formulation of a quantitative theory for prediction of drying behavior in the falling-rate period. This is a substantial handicap in drying calculations because while the constant-rate period covers the major fraction of the moisture content range, the falling-rate period generally constitutes the more difficult and more time-consuming portion of the drying process.

REFERENCES

(1) T. K. Sherwood, *Transactions*, American Institute of Chemical Engineers, Vol. 32, 1936, p. 150.

(2) N. H. Ceaglsky and O. H. Hougen, *Transactions*, American Institute of Chemical Engineers, Vol. 33, 1937, p. 283.

(3) O. H. Hougen, H. J. McCauley, and W. R. Marshall, *Transactions*, American Institute of Chemical Engineers, Vol. 36, 1940, p. 183.

(4) J. F. Pearse, T. R. Oliver, and D. M. Newitt, *Transactions*, Institute of Chemical Engineers, Vol. 27, 1949, p. 1.

(5) A. H. Nissan, W. G. Kaye, and J. R. Bell, *Journal*, American Institute of Chemical Engineers, Vol. 5, 1959, p. 103.

(6) A. H. Nissan, H. H. George, Jr., and T. V. Bolles, *Journal*, American Institute of Chemical Engineers, Vol. 6, 1940, p. 406.

(7) A. V. Luikov, *International Journal Heat Mass Transfer*, Vol. 6, 1963, p. 559.

(8) A. V. Luikov, *International Chemical Engineering*, Vol. 3, 1963, p. 195.

(9) J. W. Bartlett, Ph.D. Thesis, Rennselaer Polytechnic Inst., Troy, N. Y., 1961.

(10) E. F. Adams, Ph.D. Thesis, Rennselaer Polytechnic Inst., Troy, N. Y., 1962.

(11) W. F. Cowan, Ph.D. Thesis, Institute of Paper Chemistry, Lawrence College, Appleton, Wis., 1961.

(12) O. Krischer, *Die Wissenschlaftlichen Grundlagen der Trocknungstechnik*, Springer-Verlag, Berlin, 1956, p. 252.

(13) A. H. Nissan, D. Hansen, and J. L. Walker, *Chemical Engineering Progress Symposium Series*, Vol. 59, 1963, p. 114.

(14) A. V. Luikov and Y. A. Mikhaylov, *Theory of Energy and Mass Transfer*, Prentice Hall, Englewood Cliffs, N. J., 1961.

(15) A. H. Nissan and D. Hansen, *Journal*, American Institute of Chemical Engineers, Vol. 6, 1960, p. 606.

(16) A. H. Nissan and H. H. George, *Journal*, American Institute of Chemical Engineers, Vol. 7, 1961, p. 635.

(17) D. Hansen and B. R. Wright, "Drying of Sheet Materials with High Intensity Infrared Radiation," *TAPPI*, Dec., 1964.

DISCUSSION

M. S. Abrams[1]—This paper summarizes the most pertinent, recent information available on the drying of porous materials. Some of the references contain refined experimental techniques and their results should contribute to quantitative analyses of the complex phenomenon of the falling-rate period. In addition, certain features of these techniques may be useful in investigating the drying process in porous materials, such as cement paste.

[1] Senior research engineer, Fire Research Laboratory, Research and Development Laboratories, Portland Cement Assn., Skokie, Ill.

S. E. Pihlajavaara of Finland has investigated concrete drying and described the drying process in terms of drying-rate periods. For concrete, however, the constant-rate period is of very short duration, but the falling-rate period extends over long periods of time. Also, the amount of water lost in each period of Pihlajavaara's analysis differs greatly from that described under classical drying theory. These phenomena are probably related to the difference in pore size and pore geometry of concrete as compared with the type of material referred to by Mr. Hansen.

MOISTURE CONTENT OF WOOD IN BUILDINGS

By A. F. Verrall[1]

Synopsis

The moisture content of wood in buildings must be considered in terms of ranges likely to occur in different parts of buildings in different climatic areas. Accurate data are still insufficient to establish even ranges of moisture contents with certainty. The material presented here was pieced together from many fragmentary reports and is subject to revision as more complete data are secured.

The actual moisture contents in a given building will depend on: (1) The moisture conditions inside as influenced by the amount of vapor released, ventilation, type of heating plant, and refrigeration, (2) The degree of moisture control in crawl spaces, attics, and walls by ventilation, vapor barriers, and thermal insulation, and (3) The amount of protection afforded the exterior from rain seepage by roof overhang, gutters, and the applications of water-repellent preservatives.

Moisture contents can be greatly in excess of those in Table 1 when building design permits even, moderate rain seepage or condensation.

The moisture content of wood in service is variable. The literature consists mainly of averages for wood in different parts of buildings and as influenced by climate and season. Data are insufficient even for speculation about average moisture contents of wood in contact with soil, or in bridges and similar fully exposed structures. The averages probably are applicable to most wood in buildings. However, certain factors will be discussed which may cause above-average moisture contents in certain parts of buildings. The moisture content of wood in buildings designed to prevent wetting by rain or other liquid water is determined partly by temperature and mostly by relative humidity (RH). The average moisture contents are all below fiber saturation (28 to 32 per cent of the oven-dry weight of the wood). Thus, we are dealing with bound water within the cell wall and not free water in the air spaces within wood. Free water is present only with the disturbing factors to be mentioned later.

It must be remembered that wood in use frequently is not uniformly moist throughout its thickness. Even in $\frac{7}{8}$-in. subflooring one surface may have a moisture content 4 percentage points higher than the other. Such gradients are due to the loss or the uptake of vapor or liquid water with changing conditions.

Effect of Climate, Season, and Location in Building

Interior Finish Woodwork:

Much of the information on the moisture content of wood in buildings was derived from periodic weighing of thin,

[1] Chief, Division of Forest Disease Research, Southern Forest Experiment Station, Forest Service, U.S. Department of Agriculture, New Orleans, La.

unpainted wood slats exposed inside buildings. In extensive exposures of this type the U. S. Forest Products Laboratory (1)[2] found average moisture contents of 4 to 12 per cent in January (Fig. 1) and 4 to 13 per cent in July (Fig. 2). Seasonal variation is least in the coastal areas and greatest in the Great Lakes region. More intensive samplings in restricted areas (2,3) agree closely with these averages (Figs. 3 to 5).

Although unfinished wood slats are more sensitive to humidity fluctuations than wood that is painted or varnished, the averages in Figs. 1 and 2 probably are applicable to most interior finish items, such as doors, flooring, cabinets, and baseboards. However, conditions may

fluctuations in these slats were compared with those in similar slats exposed indoors at Berkeley (Fig. 3). Yearly averages for slats exposed outdoors in eight climatic regions of California were 1.2 to 1.7 times those for indoor exposures. For five of the regions the ratios were 1.4 to 1.5. Although specific averages for other sections of the country have not been determined, extensive periodic observations show that exterior woodwork tends to have moisture contents of 8 to 18 per cent—higher than interior woodwork—even where no rain seepage exists.

Framing and Sheathing:

These parts constitute the largest

TABLE 1—RANGES OF AVERAGE MOISTURE CONTENT, PER CENT.

Part of Structure	Moist Coastal Areas and Southeast States	Arid Southwest	Rest of Country
Interior woodwork..........................	7 to 14	4 to 7	5 to 11
Exposed exterior woodwork.................	8 to 18	?	6 to 16
Sheathing and framing:			
Substructure.............................	9 to 19	?	9 to 19
Walls and roofs..........................	8 to 14	?	6 to 14

vary considerably with type of heating system or other factors influencing relative humidity. The virtual disappearance of open gas heaters and the common use of air conditioning probably has materially reduced average moisture contents of most interior woodwork in the South, so that for this region the averages in Fig. 1 may be slightly high. However, there are no data on this.

Wood Exposed on the Exterior:

Averages for wood exposed on the exterior of buildings are available only for California (3). They are based on moisture contents of unpainted slats exposed outdoors but protected from rainwetting and direct sun. Seasonal

[2] The boldface numbers in parentheses refer to the list of references appended to this paper.

volume use of wood in buildings, and also show a greater range of normal moisture contents within an individual building than do other wood items.

Hopkins (4), using fixed electrodes in the framing of a new house in Baton Rouge, La., found that roof rafters varied little from 8 to 9 per cent moisture content over a 2-year period (Fig. 6). Slats exposed in an attic at Raleigh, N. C., fluctuated from 8 to 11 per cent, and were highest in fall (Fig. 4). Roof sheathing probably has about the same moisture contents as rafters.

Data for studs are few (Fig. 6) but suggest that, in the South, studs are similar in moisture content to rafters during winter, but slightly higher in summer. A reverse relationship was found with wall sheathing at Madison, Wis.

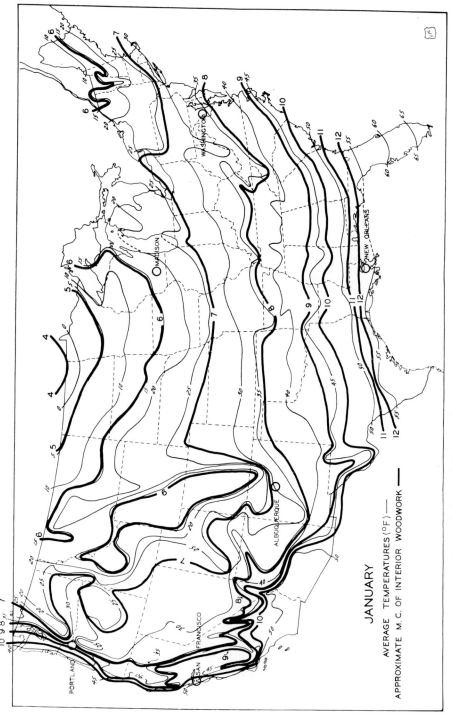

JANUARY

AVERAGE TEMPERATURES (°F) ——

APPROXIMATE M. C. OF INTERIOR WOODWORK ——

FIG. 1—Relation of Moisture Content of Interior Woodwork to Outdoor Temperature.

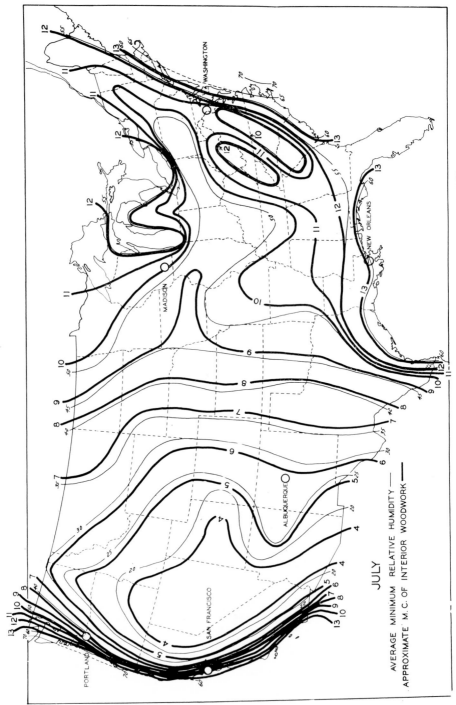

FIG. 2—Relation of Moisture Content of Interior Woodwork to Outdoor RH.

(5) (Fig. 7). Even with approved construction to minimize condensation the moisture content of sheathing rose from 6 per cent in early fall to 13 per cent during the winter.

cent during the summer. Unpublished data show that in all sections of the country bottom plates are commonly in the range from 12 to 19 per cent.

The moisture content of floor framing

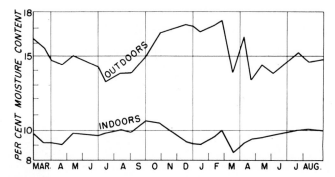

FIG. 3—Average Moisture Content of Wood Slats Exposed Indoors and Outdoors, Several Locations, California.

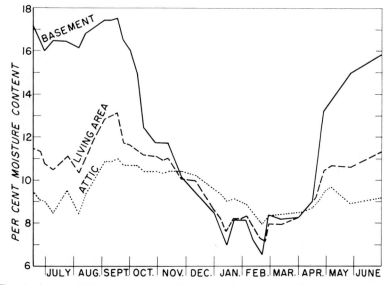

FIG. 4—Average Moisture Content of Slats Exposed Inside One House, Raleigh, N. C.

Substructures (sole plates on concrete slabs and sills, joists, and subflooring over crawl space or basements) tend to be moister than other framing and sheathing. In the Baton Rouge house (Fig. 6) the bottom plate was at 9 to 11 per cent during winter and 11 to 13 per

and subflooring over basements in the Southeast varies greatly with season (Figs. 4, 5), from about 7 per cent in the winter to 15 to 17 per cent in the summer. In limited observations elsewhere in the Gulf States (unpublished data) summer moisture contents of wood in

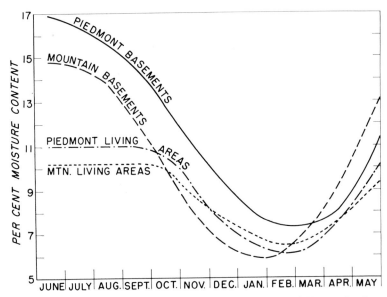

Fig. 5—Average Moisture Content of Slats Exposed in Several Houses, Southeast.

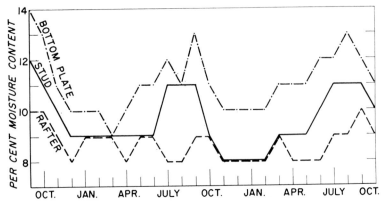

Fig. 6—Average Moisture Content of Framing in Slab-on-Ground Brick-Veneer House, Baton Rouge, La.

basements were usually 12 to 19 per cent.

In northern Illinois (6) subfloors over damp crawl spaces were at 20 per cent or above during periods when condensation occurred. They dropped to 8 to 10 per cent upon addition of a soil cover to dry the crawl space. Diller (7) reported that moisture contents of sills and girders in dry crawl spaces (with soil covers) from Maine to South Carolina remained between 10 and 18 per cent, mostly about 14 to 15 per cent. Extensive unpublished data taken over many years in the Gulf States suggest that most substructure wood in well-ventilated crawl spaces averages 12 to 15 per cent regardless of soil moisture conditions. Above a poorly ventilated, wet crawl space, moisture contents may be higher but seldom

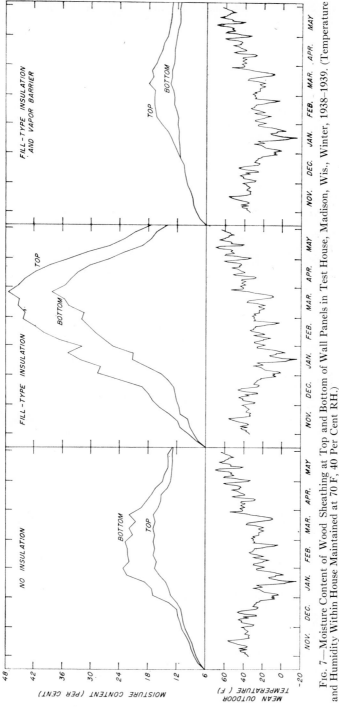

Fig. 7—Moisture Content of Wood Sheathing at Top and Bottom of Wall Panels in Test House, Madison, Wis., Winter, 1938–1939. (Temperature and Humidity Within House Maintained at 70 F, 40 Per Cent RH.)

exceed 20 per cent unless condensation has occurred.

Disturbing Factors

The moisture content of wood in buildings will rise above fiber saturation (28 to 32 per cent) only when free water is added by condensation, rain, or leakages.

The two most important types of condensation are cold-weather condensation and that associated with refrigeration in warm climates. Substantial winter condensation, although mainly a northern problem, sometimes occurs on the

and any wood used in the construction. With normal refrigeration of living and work space, only a small proportion of buildings examined in the South showed accumulations of condensate. When found, it was usually restricted to floors over wet crawl spaces. Even though condensation is uncommon, wood between air-cooled space and the outdoors or nonconditioned space tends to have a higher moisture content than wood in buildings which are not air conditioned. As vapor migrates toward air-cooled space the drop in temperature raises the RH and the equilibrium wood moisture

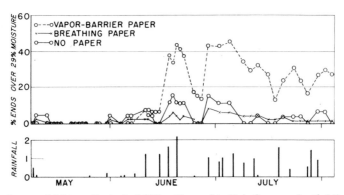

Fig. 8—Average Moisture Content of Siding Exposed to Rain Seepage, South Mississippi.

Gulf Coast. In severe cases sheathing and framing in walls, attics, and crawl spaces become water soaked, or wall voids fill with ice. Figure 7 shows expectations under more average conditions of temperature and humidity. These data are from an experimental house at Madison, Wis. (5). The danger is in walls and roofs having thermal insulation but inadequate vapor barriers, or in substructures over wet crawl spaces without vapor barrier cover. In modern construction this type of condensation can be made uncommon.

Temperature and vapor-pressure gradients also are created by air conditioning (8). When temperatures are greatly reduced, as in cold-storage rooms, condensate commonly saturates insulation

content. In a New Orleans building, subfloor moisture contents were 15 per cent under rooms without air conditioning and 22 to 25 per cent beneath those with air conditioning. In most cases measured increases were less. Although data are lacking it seems probable that less change occurs in walls and ceilings.

Rain seepage undoubtedly causes more wood wetting than any other water source. Again the amount of wetting depends on climate and building design, particularly width of roof overhang, height of wall, permeability of the wall to inward movement of vapor, and whether the exterior woodwork has been treated with a water repellent (9). The amount of rainwater accumulating in siding on an eaveless building in south

Mississippi is shown in Fig. 8. As roof overhang is increased, wetting lessens and tends to be more concentrated at joints. Except at the roof edge rain wetting is negligible on 1-story buildings with roof overhangs in excess of 24 in., even in the dampest parts of the country.

Disturbing factors may greatly change the wood moisture contents expected in buildings, and it is concluded that those with excessive moisture have been built in violation of well-known practices and standards. Moisture excesses due to rain seepage remain the chief offenders.

REFERENCES

(1) E. C. Peck, "Moisture Content of Wood in Use," U. S. Forest Service, *Forest Products Laboratory Report, No. 1655,* 1955, reissued 1961.

(2) P. J. Bois, "Wood Moisture Content in Homes—Seasonal Variations in the Southeast," *Forest Products Journal,* Vol. 9, No. 11, 1959, pp. 427–430.

(3) H. H. Smith, E. L. Ellwood, and R. W. Erickson, "Survey of the Moisture Content of Wood in Use in California," *California Forestry and Forest Products,* University of California, No. 16, Nov., 1959.

(4) W. C. Hopkins, "Moisture Content of House Framing," *Forest Products Journal,* Vol. 12, No. 7, 1962, pp. 363–366.

(5) L. V. Teesdale, "Condensation Problems in Modern Buildings," *Forest Products Labora-* *tory Report, No. 1196,* U. S. Forest Service, 1959.

(6) C. S. Moses, "Condensation and Decay Prevention under Basementless Houses," *Forest Products Laboratory Report, No. 2010,* U. S. Forest Service, 1954.

(7) J. D. Diller, "Soil Cover Reduces Decay Hazard of Basementless Houses," *Forest Pathology Special Release, No. 38,* U. S. Department of Agriculture, 1956.

(8) A. F. Verrall, "Condensation in Air-cooled Buildings," *Forest Products Journal,* Vol. 12, No. 11, 1962, pp. 531–536.

(9) A. F. Verrall, "Factors Leading to Possible Decay in Wood Siding in the South," *Forest Pathology Special Release, No. 39,* U. S. Department of Agriculture, 1953.

DISCUSSION

J. R. GASKILL[1]—I suggest that the data showing outside wood members to contain more moisture than inside members in California are not representative of the whole state at all seasons.

[1] Health and safety engineer, Research and Development Section, Hazards Control Dept., University of California Lawrence Radiation Laboratory, Livermore, Calif.

A. F. VERRALL (*author*)—There are exceptions, but in the California studies cited the average annual outdoor moisture contents were greater than indoors at all 23 stations tested. This also applied to 22, 19, 23, and 23 of the stations for spring, summer, fall, and winter averages, respectively.

THE KILN DRYING OF WOOD

By Raymond C. Rietz[1]

Synopsis

The rate at which wood in the form of rough-sawn sawmill products can be safely dried is determined by its structure and physical properties. Water moves out predominately by diffusion. Drying conditions must be controlled to prevent defects occurring because of shrinkage stresses.

Two war periods stimulated drying research and equipment design. Prior to World War I, dry kilns were of the natural circulation type and often described as "hot boxes." Modern dry kiln equipment features forced-air circulation with automatic reversal of air flow direction, automatic dry- and wet-bulb temperature control, and controlled venting. The application of impingement drying processes is gaining favor. Kiln drying schedules to accelerate the drying rate and to minimize defect formation have been greatly improved. Time-based program controllers are being given industrial trial. Moisture content quality control is being attained to assure users of fabricated wood items better performance, enhancing satisfaction.

For most uses, wood must be dried prior to the fabrication of the finished item. Furniture, for example, is assembled from parts cut from rough-sawn boards that are kiln dried to fairly low moisture content levels. Planer mill items at softwood sawmills are run from rough-sawn boards or pieces of dimension lumber that are kiln dried first. Although rough-sawn sawmill products in some instances are kiln dried to reduce weight and shipping costs, the major objective is to allow shrinkage to occur prior to fabrication of the item. Wood changes in dimension as its moisture content varies. By drying the rough-sawn sawmill product to a moisture value at which seasonal changes cannot result in much dimensional change, a more satisfactory consumer product is created.

Important reasons for drying wood, other than preshrinkage and weight reduction, are: (1) drying reduces the likelihood of stain or decay developing in transit, storage, or subsequent use, (2) most strength properties of wood increase as it is dried below a moisture content of about 30 per cent, (3) joints made with common fasteners (nails and screws) are stronger in seasoned wood, (4) glued wood products can be expected to perform better when assembled from dry wood, (5) successful treatment of wood with preservatives requires drying prior to treatment for best results, (6) dry wood is less susceptible to possible damage by insects, (7) dry wood machines better, (8) dry, machined wood takes finishes better, (9) the electrical resistance of dry wood is much greater than wet wood, and (10) dry wood is a better thermal insulating material than wet wood. The drying of wood is there-

[1] Seasoning specialist, Division of Solid Wood Products, Forest Products Laboratory, Forest Service, U.S. Department of Agriculture, Madison, Wis.

fore considered a science of moisture reduction without damaging the material and of conditioning it for its ultimate use.

WOOD-MOISTURE RELATIONS

Water is held by wood in two ways. Water enclosed within the cell cavity is called free, or capillary, water while that absorbed within the cell wall is called existing in the cell cavity, is called the fiber-saturation point. More energy is required to drive off water below the fiber-saturation point and large changes in the physical and mechanical properties of the wood occur as bound water is evaporated.

The movement of moisture in drying wood is highly complicated. Normally,

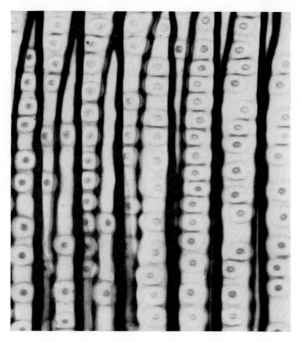

FIG. 1—Photomicrograph of Radial Section of Shortleaf Pine Magnified 250 Times. The Tubular Cells or Tracheids Have Connecting Passageways That Are Circular Openings Called Bordered Pits.

bound water. Whereas free water is not in close association with the wood substance, bound water is held by a polar attraction to the polymolecular structure of the cell wall. Since it is so bound, the moisture content of the cell wall is influenced by the vapor pressure of the air to which it is exposed.

In drying wood, free water will leave the cell first, then bound water will be evaporated. The point at which the cell wall is saturated, with no free water moisture moves from points of high to lower concentration, or in response to a moisture content gradient. It moves through passageways which collectively make up the capillary structure. These passageways are: (1) cell cavities, (2) pit chambers and their pit-membrane openings (Figs. 1 and 2), (3) resin ducts in certain softwoods and the intercellular spaces in all softwoods and hardwoods, (4) wood ray cells, and (5) transitory cell-wall passageways. The resin ducts are not very effective in moisture movement since they are usually clogged with resin; the ray cells and intercellular spaces are also relatively unimportant.

The forces that impel moisture movement are capillary forces, vapor pressure differences, and moisture content differences. When green or freshly sawn wood is dried, free evaporation will occur at the surface and stimulate capillary flow. Unfortunately, movement of water by capillary action cannot continue indefinitely. As soon as the surface fibers reach the fiber-saturation point or lower, the continuous columns are destroyed. Any free water in the cell cavities will then be absorbed by the cell walls.

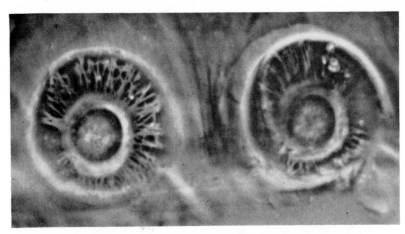

Fig. 2—Photomicrograph of Bordered Pit Cavities of Douglas Fir Magnified 2000 Times. Openings Between Network of Fiber-like Strands Surrounding Central Portion of Pit Membrane Are Passageways Through Which Water Vapor Moves.

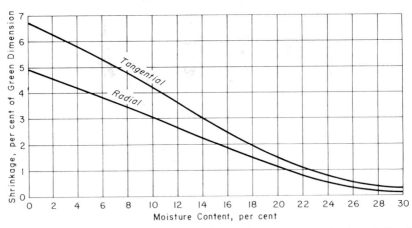

Fig. 3—Typical Moisture Content-Shrinkage Curves for Douglas Fir and Southern Yellow Pine.

ment are capillary forces, vapor pressure differences, and moisture content differences. When green or freshly sawn wood is dried, free evaporation will occur at the surface and stimulate capillary flow. Unfortunately, movement of water by capillary action cannot continue

By contrast, water vapor and bound water are moved by diffusion by differences in vapor pressure and moisture content. Since water movement by capillary action is not effective very long during the drying process, most of the moisture is removed by diffusion.

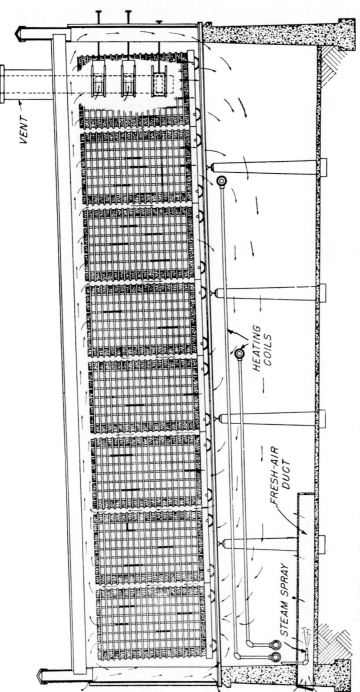

FIG. 4—Cross-Piled Natural Circulation Lumber Dry Kiln Operated Progressively. Green Lumber Placed in Kiln at Green End (*Right*) and As Dried Loads Move Toward Dry or Discharge End (*Left*). Difference in Dry-Bulb Temperature Between Two Ends Governed by Heating System Design. Venting Controlled by Manual Adjustment of Vent Stack Slot Openings.

Wood begins to shrink when bound water is removed. If wood did not shrink during drying, most of the difficulties related to the drying process would disappear. Shrinkage is responsible for a decrease in dimension, loss of footage, distortion in cross section, warping, surface and end checking, honeycombing, drying stresses, and casehardening. Wood shrinks most in the direction of the annual growth rings (tangentially), somewhat less across the rings (radially), and very little, as a rule, along the grain (longitudinally). The combined effects of radial and tangential shrinkage coupled with cross grain may cause serious distortions and warp. A moisture-shrinkage relationship is shown in Fig. 3. The drying process must be controlled to keep the development of defects associated with shrinkage to a minimum; yet the wood must be dried to a moisture content that will assure little subsequent dimensional change.

The economics of kiln drying have been a definite factor in the production of lumber and its processing. As the value of rough-sawn sawmill products increased, inventory costs, and grade and volume losses from drying defects in the air-drying process, stimulated the conversion to kiln drying green lumber items. In kiln drying the drying process is controlled so that grade can be maintained and moisture content of the dried product held to the needs of the product being fabricated. Sawmills producing softwoods are generally equipped with dry kilns so that most of the mill production can be kiln dried immediately after sawing. More and more hardwood species are being kiln dried green from the saw at an economic advantage to the mill owner.

Development of Dry Kiln Designs

The improvements in kiln design and methods of operation were greatly influenced by conditions during World Wars I and II. Prior to World War I, lumber dry kilns were generally of the natural circulation type with some dry-bulb temperature control and manual venting. These kilns were often called hot boxes. Hardwoods were air dried at the producing mills and then kiln dried at the woodworking factories in natural circulation kilns. The lumber was often conditioned for moisture content and stress relief by storage on stickers in a tempering room, although temperature and relative humidity (RH) control in these storage rooms or areas was unknown. The larger softwood sawmills often kiln dried a portion of their production, generally the better grades, in progressive, natural circulation dry kilns (Fig. 4). The methods employed to stack the lumber for kiln drying more or less designated the kiln type (that is, end-piled, cross-piled, or vertical-piled). Kilns were steam heated with the coils underneath the load and, depending upon the designer and manufacturer, ventilated in a number of different ways.

During this era condenser kilns were used to some extent. Instead of venting the kilns to reduce RH, a coil was mounted on a side wall and cold water was pumped through it, condensing water vapor which was collected in a trough and piped out of the kiln. A few external blower kilns were in operation prior to World War I, but the advantage of forced-air circulation within the kiln was not exploited. The inability to control RH probably was the major obstacle.

World War I Influences on Dry Kiln Design:

The need for greatly increased volumes of dry softwood lumber during the World War I period created an increasing demand for kilns to dry these species green from the saw. The dry kilns installed were generally natural circulation progressive dryers, and end-piled kilns were favored.

However, the acceleration of dried hardwood production was another matter. In order to keep degrade losses within limits, it was essential that in the initial phases of kiln drying green hardwoods (walnut gunstocks or vehicle material for wagons and artillery items) RH be maintained and controlled at high levels.

During this period, the merits of the superheated steam kilns were demonstrated in respect to the initial drying conditions. At this time, the Forest Products Laboratory developed the design principles of the water spray kiln to control RH. Installation of these kilns at a number of plants provided a way of greatly reducing the time to kiln dry wood green from the saw, and still keep losses from drying defects to an acceptable minimum. Drying studies at the Laboratory's water spray kilns indicated a more rapid drying rate than experienced in natural circulation kilns, apparently from a higher rate of air circulation. In developing improved schedules to reduce kiln time and drying losses due to defects, ways and means of creating more positive circulation through the stickered loads were investigated. From these studies came the basic concepts of the internal fan dry kiln, patented by the Federal government and dedicated to public use.

Early in the 1920's, RH control by regulation of dry- and wet-bulb temperatures was developed, and instrument manufacturers provided the recorder-controllers for the desired automatic control. With these instruments and the basic ideas of forced-air circulation by internal fans, the foundation for industrial development was established. Field demonstration proved the merits

of forced-air circulation, and dry kiln companies picked up the concepts of the internal fan kiln design and developed improvements that met industry needs at that time.

During World War I and for some years after, the successful operation of dry kilns became a craft encumbered with numerous secrets and unlikely concepts of how wood dries. The dry kiln operator often kept the recorder-controller in closed cabinets under lock and key. Often, even plant management did not have access to these drying secrets. Drying technology, however, gradually emerged and by 1930 many of the mysteries were replaced by sound technical concepts. The water spray and natural circulation dry kilns were now obsolete. Even the external blower kiln design, which had a surge of popularity, succumbed to various designs of the internal fan dry kiln.

Late in the 1920's the need for information on moisture content in use was evident and studies enabled the Forest Products Laboratory to recommend moisture content standards for many uses. In turn, the moisture content standards for softwood-producing mills were established by a regional trade association.

During the Depression, progress in dry kiln development was arrested, but the development of schedules for more efficient use of the improved kiln equipment was always a suitable subject for wood drying research.

World War II Influences on Dry Kiln Development:

Just before World War II, engineering attention was being focused on the economic advantages of vent control to reduce the heat losses caused by excessive ventilation, and on reversing circulation through the stacked loads of lumber to reduce drying time. Commercial installations of new instrumentation were tried. The advantages were exploited extensively during the World War II period, since energy consumption per pound of water evaporated and increased kiln output were matters of considerable concern.

This period uncovered a great need for schedules. Greater attention was paid to equalization to reduce moisture content variability and conditioning to reduce drying stresses. The need to reduce manpower requirements led to the development of improved sorters, stackers, and take-down equipment. Air drying yards were converted from hand-stacking

Fig. 5—Air Drying Yard Designed for Unit Package Handling. Carriers Transport Packages of Stickered Lumber from Stacker to Yard Where Lift Trucks Pile Packages. Pile Tops Covered for Protection.

increased operational efficiency of the installed dry kiln equipment. Dry kilns needed tuning up to meet the more exacting requirements of military needs, and training dry kiln operators in modern technology was evident. Programs to carry out these objectives were sponsored by some of the military agencies. The need to kiln dry lumber to low moisture contents with a higher degree of uniformity resulted in improved kiln drying

operations to unit package-handling systems (Fig. 5). After air drying, the units of stickered lumber were placed in package-loaded kilns of new design or loaded on kiln trucks for drying in conventional kilns (Fig. 6). The switch to further automation in handling lumber for drying continued.

During and after the War, research attention was directed toward the more fundamental aspects of drying schedules.

Researchers are still seeking the factors that influence drying rate as related to defect control, and the preservation of both physical and mechanical wood properties. In the past, drying schedule development was generally empirical and improvements were blocked by the lack of fundamental knowledge of what occurs during the drying process. Today research continues and patterns of drying schedule arrangement are being evolved for pilot testing and commercial adaptation (Fig. 7).

Since World War II some of the special drying processes (such as vapor drying, solvent drying, superheated steam drying, and high-frequency dielectric heating) have been given pilot scale and commercial trial. The ventilated forced-air circulation lumber dry kiln, however,

FIG. 6—Package Loaded Lumber Dry Kiln. Unit Packages of Stickered Lumber Placed in Internal Fan Ventilated Dry Kiln with Lift Truck.

has not been replaced as suitable equipment for an economic drying process.

Present Situation:

The designers of forced-air circulation

Drying conditions are automatically controlled in both directly and indirectly heated dry kilns by controlling the dry- and wet-bulb temperatures. The thermal elements of the recorder-controller for

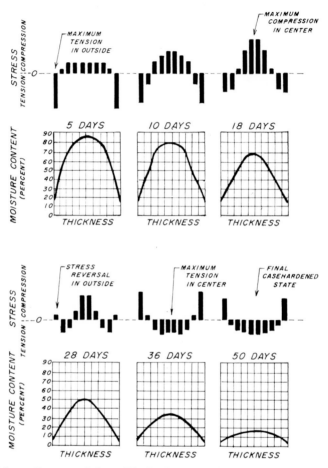

Fig. 7—Moisture Content and Stress Distributions at Various Stages of Drying 2-in. Red Oak. Drying Schedule Patterns Are Developed from Research Data.

ventilated dry kilns have gradually incorporated higher air circulation rates across the loads of stickered lumber. The power requirements are now considerable, but increased power costs are economically justified as the desired moisture content is gained in a shorter kiln time.

dry-bulb control are either of the dual type or located in such a position that, regardless of the direction of air circulation, the entering air dry-bulb temperature is controlled by the instrument. The wet-bulb thermal element is conveniently located so that the wicks can be replaced readily. Automatic venting and fresh air intake are obtained through wet-bulb control instrumentation. Air-operated controllers are still the most popular type of instruments installed; the wet-bulb thermometry is so arranged that, when the wet-bulb temperature exceeds the set point, the vents connected by linkage to an air motor valve are opened. As the wet-bulb dips to near the set point the vents close, but the actual wet-bulb temperature would have to drop somewhat below setting before the steam spray or other forms of adding water vapor are turned on.

A recent innovation makes the venting quite positive by pumping fresh air into

rangement remain competitive. One of the features that has influenced the design of the kiln structure is the elimination of the pit in the lumber dry kiln. Thus, prefabricated dry kilns are now available and their increased cost is offset, it is claimed, by a longer life and higher resale value (Fig. 8).

The smaller sawmill using electric power has made the operation of steam-heated dry kilns an economic problem. Even though the fuel, such as sawdust, shavings, or hogged fuel, may be available at a comparatively low cost, the justification of a boiler installation manned around the clock often cannot

Fig. 8—Prefabricated Lumber Dry Kiln with Overhead Internal Fans. Control Equipment Housed in Operating Room Above Doors.

the dryer with a blower; the increased pressure forces air out of the kiln at the vents. A possible advantage: venting could be made at a location irrespective of the air circulating system so that at times, at least, exhausted air is taken from the leaving-air side of the load of lumber.

The great bulk of kiln dried softwoods are dried on the basis of time schedules. That is, the operator resets the recorder-controller to the desired dry- and wet-bulb temperatures on the basis of time in the kiln. Surprisingly, relatively few program controllers are in use having precut cams or other devices for adjusting the recorder-controller setting as a function of time in the kiln.

Various systems of internal fan ar-

be warranted. The gas-fired dry kiln fits this situation, and both direct-fired and indirect-heating units are being used. The availability of water vapor for conditioning the kiln charge is often a problem and, in some instances, an auxiliary gas-fired steam boiler is installed for this purpose. In other instances the dry kiln is a conventional steam-heated unit but the boiler is gas fired and attendance is not required when operated at low steam pressures. After the gas has been burned, the products of combustion are pumped into the kiln to gain greater heat recovery from the purchased natural gas.

With circulation rates in conventional dry kilns reaching an economic limit, more knowledge is needed regarding boundary layer influence and heat and mass transfer effects on the wood drying rate. Veneer dryers are now using impingement or jet air streams perpendicular to the moving sheet to provide the heat needed to evaporate the water. The drying rate has been significantly increased compared with that obtained with more conventional systems of air circulation in the veneer dryers. The possible applicability to wood in lumber sizes has not been explored.

As resources of old-growth timber are used up and the nation must rely more and more on young growth, it becomes apparent that the grain patterns of the boards cut from the smaller logs create problems of controlling warp. It seems likely that improved thickness control in the sawmill, coupled with better stacking methods and, perhaps, hold-down devices to increase the restraint to warp, are developments to be anticipated.

Control of surface checking or its prevention in the drying and utilization of the more refractory species of wood has not been extensively developed. Until research finds a way to treat green wood economically so that the whole cross section will not shrink, we must learn how to treat the surfaces so that surface checking is minimized. The effect on surface checking of presurfacing or kiln drying boards that are planed prior to drying is being investigated, and the results appear to have economic possibilities. The combination of presurfacing green lumber followed by a rather superficial chemical treatment offers greater opportunity to control the defect—and do it economically—than if the chemical were used alone.

IMPORTANCE OF MOISTURE CONTENT QUALITY AND CONTROL

The necessity to dry wood prior to the fabrication of a product, such as furniture, has long been known. Recently, better heating and air conditioning introduced new problems. The conversion of heating systems to provide comfort in all the rooms of our homes, factories, offices, and public places, has created a situation requiring better knowledge of the environment of wood use. The fabricating industries discovered from experience that kiln drying to lower moisture content levels was essential, but the degree of dryness and the variation in dryness that could be tolerated were not well known.

Moisture content of wood in use surveys were conducted by the Forest Products Laboratory in the late 1920's, and the recommendations developed from those investigations are still generally quite satisfactory. The more general use of air conditioning involving dehumidification as well as cooling, and humidification coupled with heating, has influenced the moisture content of wood in use, and extensive studies have not been carried out to indicate the advantage to wood performance. The experiences of the hardwood fabricators, however, seem to indicate that comfort conditioning is an advantage as extremes of dryness and high moisture content of the wood are diminished.

Although softwood structural members are sometimes used in building construction without prior drying, the trend toward greater use of dried items is definitely increasing. If the standards for lumber sizes are to be associated with a moisture content requirement, drying prior to machining to size is essential. Large timbers will be used in the green condition as before. Drying takes place while in use. The laminated beam, on the other hand, is assembled from dried lumber items to assure good bonding performance and maintenence of dimensional stability in use.

The producers of softwood lumber

items for the building industry will provide dried and finished material. The kiln drying equipment needed to meet the more refined moisture content requirements will no doubt be a significant improvement as compared with kilns in operation. At the same time, however, the suitability of new and different drying processes which might accomplish the drying in a shorter time with less degrade will certainly be investigated.

Hardwood lumber has characteristically been air dried and shipped to the processor in that condition. The hardwood processing plants usually had their own dry kiln equipment so that the moisture content requirements for fabricating the product could be controlled. Significant changes are taking place. In some cases the secondary manufacturer is procuring green lumber and the drying process is wholly under his control. Sometimes the producer dries the rough-sawn stock to the moisture content requirements of the fabricator, so dry kilns must be installed. And, there is increasing reliance of the producer and processor on the custom kiln drying operator to dry the stock to the moisture requirements designated by the processor. These changes place greater emphasis on kiln design and operational methods that will eliminate the air drying process.

RECENT DEVELOPMENTS IN DRYER DESIGNS

The forced-air circulation ventilated dry kiln is still the most economic type of kiln equipment used by the wood-producing and wood-using industries. Both segments, however, are very definitely interested in a faster drying process that will reduce their drying costs. The advantage of increased air circulation rates has been and will continue to be an area of engineering development by the dry kiln company

engineers. Their problem is to keep power costs within reason. Redesigning to reduce energy losses due to turbulence other than that between the layers of lumber can be anticipated.

The introduction of impingement methods for heat and mass transfer in the drying of wood veneer has stimulated research to provide more knowledge regarding the influence of the boundary layer on the drying of wood.

A recent development in kiln design, construction, and installation for drying wood is the prefabricated dry kiln. For some time kiln companies provided structure designs so that local contractors could erect the building in which equipment, furnished by the dry kiln companies, could be installed. Although this is still being done, major dry kiln companies can now provide prefabricated structures which have advantages to offset their increased cost.

The ventilated lumber dry kilns waste energy. Water evaporated from the wood is carried out of the dryer as vapor at the dry-bulb temperature of the kiln. It is now cheaper to vent the dryer than it is to remove water evaporated from the wood in some other manner. Some day the latent heat of evaporation will be recovered and the water that was evaporated from the wood will be discharged from the dryer as water and at fairly low temperature. The recovered heat will be recirculated.

Excessive venting in ventilated dry kilns can waste much heat energy, since added steam is required to raise the wet-bulb temperature and incoming fresh air must be heated to the controlled dry-bulb temperature. Vent control is hooked in with wet-bulb control but, all too often, the vent caps are not tight enough and some unnecessary venting occurs. This condition is now circumvented by some dry kiln engineers by pressure venting the kiln. The additional power cost to operate the vent blower motor is presumably balanced by the increased circulation rate obtained with the fan system as some of the air delivery is not diverted.

Research and experience in the drying of wood has related the schedule of changing dry- and wet-bulb temperature with the moisture content of the item being dried. As the moisture content of the pieces making up the kiln charge at

FIG. 9—Rough-Sawn Lumber Sorted for Length and Machine Stacked. Stickers Well-Aligned to Provide Good Restraint to Warp.

any time depends upon a number of wood properties, sampling methods have been devised that require periodic weighing to determine when changes in drying conditions can be made safely. The changes are made manually by resetting the recorder-controller. To eliminate the need to prepare and weigh kiln samples periodically, the programmed controller based on time is creating increasing interest. Use of this programmed controller on kilns designed for softwoods, usually operated on the basis of time schedules,

seems logical. The technicians responsible for kiln operation must develop a more comprehensive system than that generally practiced of analyzing the initial moisture content of the kiln charge, if the drying program is to be adjusted to save needed time. It is expected that, as it becomes economic to kiln dry our hardwoods green from the saw, these time-based program controllers will find greater application.

The time-based program controller, however, is not the more automated push-button type of equipment desired by the industry. Research and development may relate the drying process to some other property of the wood more readily measured from the green condition to the desired moisture content and the information fed into a little black box that will automatically adjust the drying conditions. Unfortunately, research and development are not even near such a possibility. Good kiln drying results depend upon having good kiln drying equipment supervised by a reasonably well-trained technician.

One of the elements of drying costs is the preparation of the wood prior to kiln drying. Sorting of lumber for species, thickness, grades, length, and sometimes width is an expensive operation. The industry is supporting the development of automated sorters by installing equipment and giving it a good industrial trial. Stacking of lumber has been fairly well automated (Fig. 9). Wood stickers are used to separate the layers of lumber and provide the space for air movement, and they sometimes create problems in the magazines that feed the sticker laying devices. Usually these troubles are associated with distortions in the stickers. Substitutes for wood have been tried, but have not replaced the wood sticker. Take-down equipment of various designs is available. In the softwood sawmill the kiln dried rough lumber is fed across the dry chain for regrading and sorting for dry storage. In the woodworking plant using kiln dried hardwoods, kiln truck-loads of lumber are often placed on a lumber lift in the rough mill so that the cut-off saw operators can pull off the boards at saw table level. One man is needed to take care of the stickers.

One of the advantages of automatic lumber stacking equipment is the improved alignment of stickers and, with it, a reduction in warp of the boards. Restraining distortion in those boards so inclined because of grain patterns, abnormal wood, and normal shrinkage, results in a greater yield of products from the rough-sawn material. Placing weights on kiln truckloads has proved effective but it is seldom done because of the reduction in kiln-holding capacity. As losses from warp become more and more obvious, devices will probably be developed to restrain warp but reduce kiln-holding capacity very little.

Rough-sawn lumber often varies in thickness, creating problems in stacking for kiln drying. Poorly sawn lumber not only decreases the yield of lumber recovery from the logs but increases losses due to warp and sticker breakage. Surfacing the green lumber to produce material of a uniform thickness has definite benefits in stacking for kiln drying, and is being investigated on a commercial basis. Kiln-holding capacity is increased, warp control is better, final dryness is more uniform, and studies indicate that the more refractory hardwoods are less apt to surface check. These advantages should more than pay for the extra handling and machining involved.

CONCLUSIONS

The crafts involved in the kiln drying of wood, once considered mysterious, are now based on sound technological principles. Dry kiln equipment has evolved from natural circulation designs, with relatively poor control of drying conditions, to forced-air circulation designs having excellent automatic control of drying conditions. Drying schedule research has provided a basis for developing ways to accelerate the drying rate, yet minimize the development of drying defects. The average moisture content and required uniformity of kiln dried rough-sawn wood items can now be controlled so that the performance of finished wood products in homes, schools, etc. will give complete satisfaction.

CONCRETE DRYING METHODS AND THEIR EFFECT ON FIRE RESISTANCE

By M. S. Abrams[1] and D. L. Orals[1]

Synopsis

This paper compares laboratory methods for the conditioning of concrete prior to exposure to the standard fire test (ASTM Method E 119) using slab specimens 3 by 3 ft by 6 in. thick. In the artificial conditioning methods the specimens were exposed to heated air in a kiln controlled at temperatures to 200 F. Such kiln drying was conducted both without controlled humidity and at several selected relative humidity (RH) levels. The drying of some slabs was accelerated by infrared heat radiation. Information is given on the effect of ambient RH level in the natural drying procedure described in Method E 119.

The effect of the several drying procedures on the time requirements to reach the desired concrete test humidities, the humidity gradient through the concrete sections, and the subsequent fire endurance of the concrete slabs was evaluated in terms of the results obtained on companion slabs naturally dried in air at 73 F and 35 per cent RH. It was found that all of the artificial conditioning methods considerably reduced the time required to reach test humidity. However, the saving in conditioning time was accompanied by depressed fire endurance periods, that is, endurance periods substantially lower than those resulting from slabs naturally dried to the same test RH.

The fire-resistive properties of building materials and constructions are measured according to procedures specified in ASTM Method E 119.[2] One section of this standard defines the manner of conditioning a specimen and the moisture level to be achieved in the specimen before it can be tested. In 1959 the specification on natural drying (drying in laboratory air at normal temperature) was revised to require control of the conditioning environment at 30 to 35 per cent relative humidity (RH) and 70 to 80 F. Testing was permissible when the dampest part of any section of a specimen attained an equilibrium RH of 70 ± 5 per cent. Experience has shown that the conditioning of structural elements of concrete under the natural drying procedure often entails lengthy delays before the specified humidity level is reached. Some investigations (1–4)[3] on the fire endurance of concrete constructions in the United States and England reported waiting periods ranging from several months to over two years. Such inconveniences have given rise to efforts toward shortening the conditioning period by drying at above normal temperature to accelerate the conditioning process.

Artificial drying of fire-test specimens

---

[1] Senior and associate research engineers. respectively, Fire Research Section, Research and Development Div., Portland Cement Assn., Skokie, Ill.

[2] Methods of Fire Tests of Building Construction and Materials (E 119), *1964 Book of ASTM Standards*, Part 14.

[3] The boldface numbers in parentheses refer to the list of references appended to this paper.

is not a new idea. It has been an optional part of the standard for many years; but, the manner in which the artificial drying shall be done has not been defined. The only restriction placed on

o Thermocouple Junction

Common Lead Wire -
3 Thermocouples
in Parallel

4"

2"   2"   24 Gage
Chromel-
Alumel
Wire

$\frac{1}{8}$"

2"

1"   5$\frac{5}{8}$"

1"

$\frac{1}{2}$"
$\frac{1}{2}$"

$\frac{1}{8}$" $\frac{1}{4}$" $\frac{1}{8}$"

6"
Surface Exposed to Fire

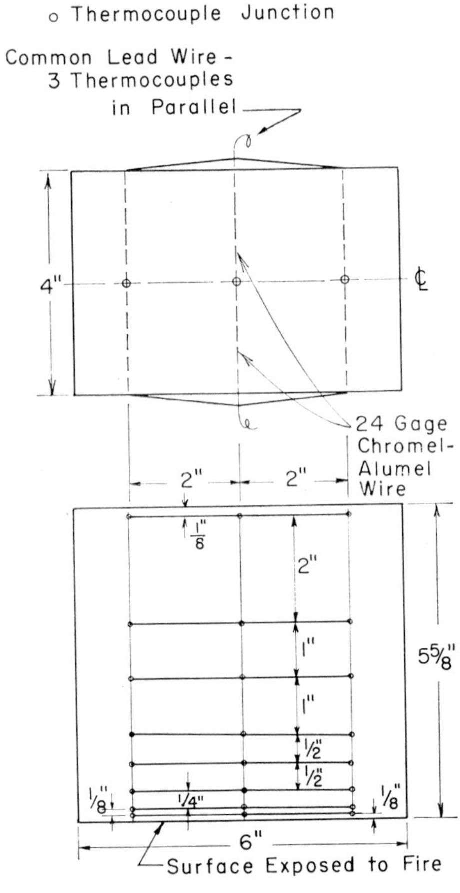

Fig. 1a—Concrete Thermocouple Instrumentation Block.

a procedure employed is that temperatures used to dry a material shall not affect its structural properties. During recent years, changes were proposed in the standard toward greater latitude in the drying temperature and in the specimen humidity level required for test from that provided in the 1959 version. However, there are practically

no published data which show the effect of the drying method on the final moisture condition of the test specimen and the consequent effect on its fire endurance.

Information obtained from pilot drying studies in the Portland Cement Association Laboratories on 3 by 3 ft by 6 in. slabs and on *I*-beam segments of concrete indicated that the humidity gradient through a specimen section was dependent on the method and time of conditioning. The results of subsequent fire tests indicated that the fire endurance of concrete, in terms of its heat

Fig. 1b—Block Positioned in 3 by 3 ft Slab Form.

transmission, was closely related to the moisture gradient at time of the fire test. It became evident that a better understanding of the complete conditioning process for fire-test specimens was necessary. This paper presents the first results of the continuing investigation undertaken for this purpose.

OBJECTIVES AND TEST PROGRAM

The objectives of this investigation were:

1. To determine the fire endurance of naturally dried concrete slabs when conditioned at various ambient RH levels to selected concrete test RH levels.

2. To investigate methods for ac-

celerating the drying of concrete fire-test specimens.

3. To determine the moisture condition resulting from various drying procedures, and to evaluate its effect on fire endurance.

Several fire-test slabs and companion humidity control slabs were cast of a single concrete mix design. All were cured initially in a fog-room for seven

artificially were stored in air at 73 F and 50 per cent RH for 21 days before exposure to artificial drying. Four artificial drying procedures were used in the investigation.

Materials, Specimens, and Equipment

Concrete:

The concrete for all specimens was of a normal-weight mix with a water-

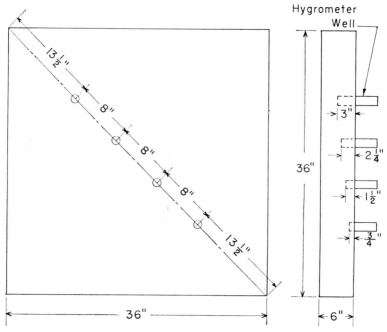

Fig. 2—Slab Specimen for Monitoring Concrete RH.

days. Slabs for natural drying were then exposed to selected ambient relative humidities until ready for the fire test. Four ambient relative humidities and three concrete test relative humidities were used in the natural drying phase of the program.[4] Specimens to be dried

---

[4] Natural drying of test slabs to the lowest established concrete RH (50 per cent) has not yet been completed. In order to extend some of the comparisons in this paper, data from an earlier drying study of slabs of similar dimensions and concrete have been substituted.

cement ratio of 0.6, a cement factor of 4.5 bags/yard[3], a 2-in. slump, no purposely entrained air, and an average 28-day cylinder strength of 4000 psi. The aggregate was a natural sand and gravel, obtained locally with a maximum size of $1\frac{1}{2}$ in. The mix proportions by weight of the concrete mix were 1:2.83: 5.26.

Fire-Test Specimen:

Slab specimens 3 by 3 ft by 6 in. thick

were used. Each of the fire-test specimens contained a concrete block insert (Figs. 1*a* and *b*) which was 6 by 4 by $5\frac{5}{8}$ in. deep, with spaced thermocouples of 24-gage chromel-alumel wire for de-

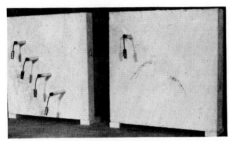

FIG. 3—Humidity Monitoring and Fire Test Slabs with Humidity Sensing Instrumentation.

termining the temperature distribution during the test. The block contained aggregate of 1-in. maximum size, and within 18 hr after fabrication was cast integrally with the fire-test slab proper. Each fire-test slab was provided with a well, formed and lined by a short length of 1-in. diameter thin-wall electrical conduit which terminated at the mid-thickness. The concrete at the bottom of the well was exposed and its RH was used to indicate the readiness of the slab for the fire test. The well was positioned about 12 in. off-center of the slab, measured along a diagonal.

Specimen for Monitoring Concrete RH:

All fire-test slabs were accompanied

throughout the curing and drying phases by a humidity control or monitoring slab. The monitoring slab was of the same dimensions as the fire-test slab and was cast at the same time. Locations of humidity wells are shown in Fig. 2. These companion monitoring slabs were used to determine the changes in the humidity gradients through the slab sections as well as to determine when the concrete humidity at middepth had reached the desired test level. Figure 3 shows specimens for monitoring concrete RH and for the fire test.

System of Measuring Concrete RH:

One of the methods used in the program to measure the concrete RH was that suggested by Menzel (5), in which an electrical hygrometer element about $\frac{3}{4}$-in. in diameter is inserted in the steel tube-lined well. The humidity of the air within the well is recorded when the moisture content of the air in the sealed well reaches equilibrium (24 to 48 hr) with the moisture content of the concrete exposed at the bottom of the well. All humidity readings obtained during this investigation were taken with concrete temperatures at 73 ± 2 F.

As a further check, humidity determinations were also made on several of the slabs with a small $\frac{3}{16}$-in. diameter electrical probe-type hygrometer that was developed recently (6). The same wells

TABLE 1—ACCELERATED DRYING EQUIPMENT.

Function	Conditions
Heated air drying without humidity control	21 by 7 by 6 ft high, steam radiation, fan-air circulation, range of temperature control 80 to 210 F.
Radiant heat drying without humidity control	10 by 3 by $4\frac{1}{2}$ ft high, infrared heat radiation lamps, temperature controlled to maintain specimen surface at 200 F, natural air convection (Fig. 4).
Heated air drying with humidity control	23 by 5 by 6 ft high, steam radiation, fan-air circulation, range of temperature control 80 to 210 F, humidity by steam injection.

Fig. 4—One Side of Infrared Radiation Heating Enclosure.

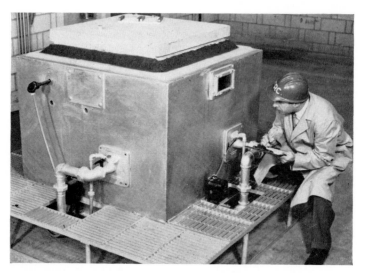

Fig. 5—Slab Furnace for Fire Tests.

in the slabs were used interchangeably for both hygrometers. Values for RH obtained with the small probe hygrometer checked within 2 percentage points of those obtained with the larger hygrometer.

Drying Facilities:

Four storage rooms and three drying kilns were used in the program. Each of the conditioning rooms was maintained at 73 ± 2 F, but at different relative

humidities; 10, 35, 50, and 75 per cent. Drying of the concrete slabs at elevated temperatures was accomplished in three kilns (Table 1).

Slab Furnace:

The small slab furnace (Fig. 5) was heated by natural gas fuel and was controlled automatically to the time-temperature relationship given in the ASTM Method E 119.

TABLE 2—DRYING PROCEDURE DETAILS.

Drying Method	Conditions		Remarks
	Environmental RH, per cent	Test RH at Mid-depth, per cent	
Natural, 73 F	10	90, 75, and 50	All surfaces of slabs exposed to conditioning environment. Humidity readings at regular and frequent intervals.
	35	90, 75, and 50	
	50	90 and 75	
	75	90	
Artificial, closed kiln at 200 F, no humidity control	Kiln humidity: 4 per cent. Test humidities: 75 or 50 per cent at mid-depth. Temperature raised to 200 F over a 12-hr period. Slabs in shut-down kilns for 24 hr to cool before removal to 75 or 50 per cent RH storage rooms for humidity determinations.		200 F chosen because effective drying could be realized without causing physico-chemical changes in concrete. Washa and Saeman (7) and Matthieu (8) showed that only small changes in structural properties occur at this temperature.
Artificial, infrared kiln at 200 F, no humidity control			

	Rehumidifying Schedule				
	Sequence of Events	Dry-Bulb Temperature, deg F	Kiln RH, per cent	Duration, days	
Artificial, at 200 F, followed by rehumidification	1	200	10	1	Concrete dried at 200 F to mid-depth RH, 5 to 8 percentage points above required test RH. Concrete then rehumidified according to schedule. Final steps of procedure provided a soaking period with kiln at RH sought in concrete. Cooled slabs removed to 75 or 50 RH storage rooms for monitoring.
	2	175	25	1	
	3	150	50	1	
	4	125	85	1	
	5	100	100	1	
	6	75	variable[a]	1	
	7	150	50 or 75[b]	7	
	8	75	variable[a]	1	

Drying Method	Conditions	Remarks
Artificial, humidity control of kiln atmosphere from beginning of procedure	Kiln temperature and humidity, 175 F and 40 per cent, maintained until concrete RH at mid-depth within 3 per cent of desired level of 50 or 75 per cent RH. Kiln then adjusted to 150 F and 50 or 75 per cent RH and maintained for four days.	Procedure directed to drying concrete at slower rate to produce a more gradual humidity gradient through section.

[a] Kiln shut down after Event 5. Kiln RH varied from 100 per cent to laboratory space value as kiln cooled.

[b] Value dependent on target test level of 50 or 75 per cent.

DRYING AND FIRE TESTING PROCEDURES

Drying Procedures:

Details of the five drying methods used in the investigation are given in Table 2.

The Fire Test:

The conditioned slabs were tested on the slab furnace unrestrained and without load. Unexposed surface temperatures were measured at four locations with chromel-alumel thermocouples under new-felted asbestos pads. Figure 6 shows the surface thermocouple arrangement. The tests were terminated when the average unexposed surface temperature rose 250 F, or when the temperature at a single point of measurement rose 325 F over that recorded at the start of test.

DISCUSSION OF RESULTS

Natural Drying:

As indicated, the principal variable in studying the natural drying of 6-in. thick concrete slabs was the storage environment RH. The temperature was maintained at 73 ± 2 F in all cases. Under controlled environmental RH of 10, 35, 50, and 75 per cent, data were sought regarding: (1) the drying time required to reduce the concrete RH at the midthickness of the slabs to three different levels—90, 75, and 50 per cent, (2) the humidity gradients within the concrete sections resulting from these

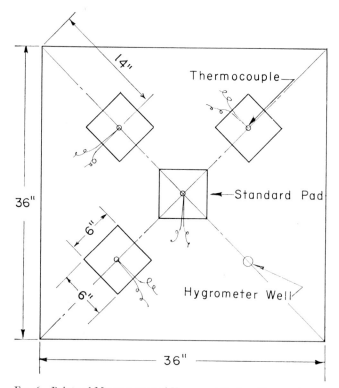

FIG. 6—Points of Measurement of Unexposed Surface Temperatures.

TABLE 3—EFFECT OF ENVIRONMENTAL HUMIDITY ON NATURAL DRYING TIME.

Environmental RH, per cent	Drying Time for Concrete Test Humidities, months		
	90% RH	75% RH	50% RH
10	0.6	2.7	20.5
35	1	3.7	28
50	1.2	8	...
75	1.2	...	...

drying exposures, and (3) the fire endurances of 6-in. thick concrete slabs so treated, as determined by the unexposed surface temperature criteria.

Drying time—The drying times necessary to reach the preselected test relative humidities are given in Table 3. There are several significant observations which can be made from these data.

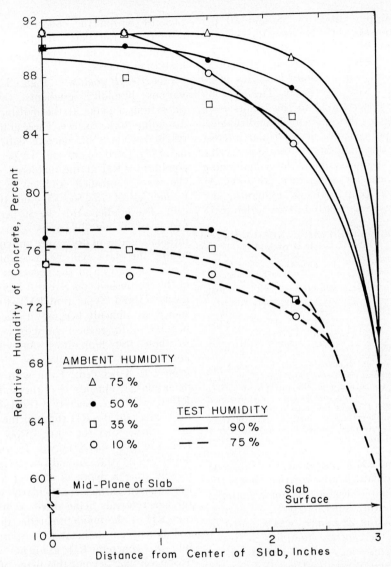

FIG. 7—Effect of Ambient Humidity on Humidity Gradient Through Slab Sections.

Although the total exposure time to reach the 90 per cent RH test level was relatively short at all of the environmental relative humidities, approximately twice as much time was required under ambient humidities of 50 and 75 per cent than under 10 per cent ambient humidity. The effect of the environ-mental RH was more pronounced when natural drying was directed to the concrete RH test level of 75 per cent. Under an ambient RH of 50 per cent, eight months elapsed before the desired middepth concrete RH of 75 per cent was achieved. Approximately $\frac{1}{2}$ and $\frac{1}{3}$ of this time was required at environmental humidities of 35 and 10 per cent, respectively. To lower the concrete RH to 50 per cent with the environmental RH controlled at 10 and 35 per cent, waiting times in excess of 20 months were necessary. The data in Table 3 pertaining to the results from drying at the ambient humidity level of 35 per cent are of particular interest since this humidity is the upper value given in the standard for conditioning specimens for acceptance fire tests. At 35 per cent ambient humidity, 3.7 months were required to dry a slab to 75

TABLE 4—FIRE ENDURANCE OF NATURALLY DRIED SLABS.

Environmental RH, per cent	Fire Endurance Time as Affected by Test Humidities, min[a]		
	90% RH	75% RH	50% RH
10	194	188	165
35	192	186	168
50	189	184	. . .
75	192	. . .	. . .

[a] Based on time for average unexposed surface temperature to rise 250 F above the initial surface temperature or the unexposed surface temperature at any one point of measurement to rise 325 F above the initial surface temperature, whichever occurs first. In each of these tests, the average temperature rise of 250 F occurred first.

per cent RH at its middepth (3 in.). As the standard is now written, this is the maximum allowable RH for a material when testing is permitted.[5]

A total of 28 months was required to reduce the concrete humidity to 50 per cent. This long waiting period (about two years) required to lower the concrete humidity at the middepth of the section from 75 to 50 per cent under an ambient humidity of 35 per cent may be qualitatively related to: (1) a diminishing differential between the vapor pressure of the environmental air and the vapor

[5] Testing is permitted if the specimen has not attained this RH after one year of exposure to air at 30 to 35 per cent RH and 70 to 80 F.

pressure within the concrete, and (2) changes in the pore structure of the cement paste which occur due to the hydration process.

Concrete RH gradients—Figure 7 shows various humidity gradients through slabs from a plane at the midthickness extending to the surface. These gradients resulted when 6-in. concrete slabs were naturally dried to 90 and 75 per cent equilibrium RH at the middepth under the four controlled ambient relative humidities of 75, 50, 35, and 10 per cent. The gradients for the 50 per cent test level are not shown, as several additional months of drying are anticipated before the data will be available. A direct comparison of the curves at each of the established concrete test humidity levels (75 and 90 per cent RH) is made somewhat difficult because it was not possible to dry each of the slabs exactly to these test humidities. As will be noted, there were deviations ranging from 2 to 4 per cent. Even with these deviations, it appears that the ambient RH at which the concrete was dried had little effect on the RH through the concrete when either the 90 or 75 per cent RH test level was attained. It will be noted that the humidity decreases rapidly from a depth of about $\frac{3}{4}$ in. to the exposed surface, particularly when the concrete was being dried to 90 per cent RH at the middepth under the 10 and 35 per cent ambient RH exposures. But the concrete RH gradients were reasonably flat beyond this plane of the section to the middle plane.

Natural drying and fire endurance—The results of the several fire tests of naturally dried slabs are given in Table 4. These data indicate that for concrete test RH of 90, 75, and 50 per cent, the ambient RH under which the slabs were dried had little effect upon their fire endurance. The slight differences of 5, 4, and 3 min shown for concrete test humidities of 90, 75, and 50 per cent, respectively, may have been due to small differences in the thermocouple pads or to small variations from the test humidities. An earlier study (9) showed been naturally dried to the concrete test RH of approximately 90 per cent at the center under ambient relative humidities of 75, 50, 35, and 10 per cent. It will be seen that the temperatures at

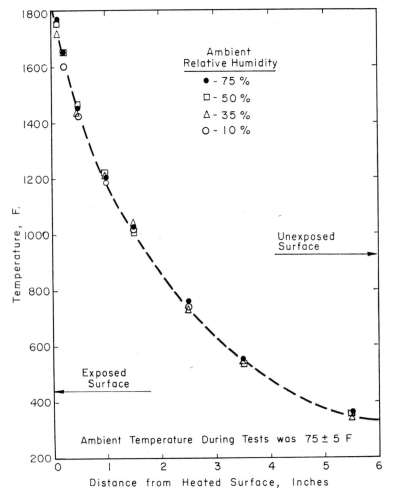

FIG. 8—Effect of Ambient RH on Temperature Distribution.

that deviations of this order can result from variations in standard thermo-couple pads, even though they are produced under rigid specifications.

Figure 8 shows the internal temperature distribution that existed at the ends of fire exposures of slabs that had the same points of measurement within the sections were quite similar. From this similarity it is reasonable to expect that the fire endurance times of the slabs, as determined by the unexposed surface temperature criteria, would also be similar. As noted from Table 4 this was the case. The remarks concerning the temperature distribution of the concrete and the resulting endurance times of the concrete also apply to slabs naturally dried to 75 and 50 per cent RH at the midthickness. Lower endurance times were obtained at the 75 and 50 per cent test humidities.

Table 4 also shows the important effect of the concrete test humidity

for corresponding points between slabs dried to 90 and 50 per cent test humidities and the slab tested at 75 per cent RH are shown after exposure to the fire for 168 min. This was the time to the end of the fire test for the slab specimen that had been dried to the concrete test humidity of 50 per cent, Table 4. At corresponding points of temperature measurement, greater differences in tem-

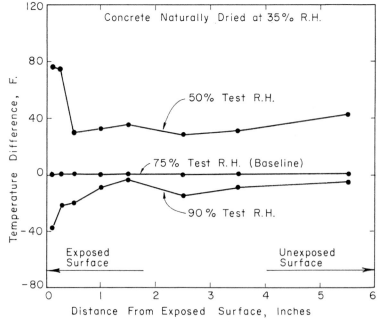

FIG. 9—Temperature Difference at Corresponding Points in Different Concrete Slabs at 168-min Exposure (168-min was the fire endurance time of slab dried at 50 per cent test RH.)

level on the fire endurance of the slabs. For slabs dried under the 35 per cent ambient humidity exposure there was a 6-min reduction in fire resistance from the 90 to 75 per cent RH test levels. Further shortening of the fire endurance time by 18 min occurred when the concrete test humidity was lowered to 50 per cent. These differences in fire endurance can be related to the temperature distribution within the concrete. In Fig. 9 the differences in temperature

peratures were obtained between slabs dried to 50 and 75 per cent RH test levels than between slabs dried to 75 and 90 per cent. The rate of rise in the unexposed surface temperature was nearly equal at 168 min for all three cases. Thus, with the same rate of temperature increase, a longer endurance time would be expected for a slab dried to 75 per cent RH than for a slab dried to 50 per cent RH. Similarly, slabs dried to 90 per cent RH would be expected to have a longer endurance time than slabs dried to 75 per cent. However, the increase would be greater in the former instance.

There are at least three major factors

of chemical reaction), (2) The amount of evaporable water available at time of the fire test, and (3) The effect of (1) and (2) on the thermal properties of the concrete. Powers and Brownyard

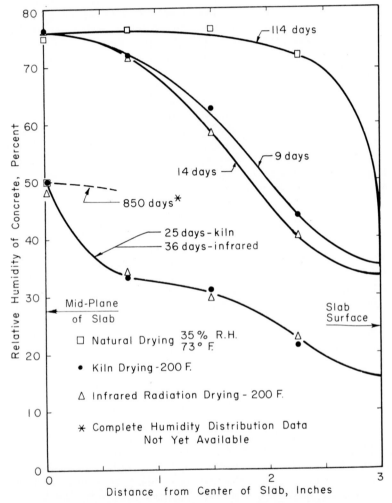

FIG. 10—RH Distributions Resulting from Natural and Artificial Drying.

to be considered in analyzing the fire test results obtained for slabs dried under the ambient RH condition of 35 per cent: (1) The degree of hydration and its relation to the amount of non-evaporable water (water held as a result

(10) and Lea and Desch (11) noted that hydration of portland cement practically ceases when the RH of portland cement paste drops below 80 to 85 per cent. Thus, it appears that there probably was an increase in the nonevaporable water

as the concrete dried from 90 to 75 per cent RH. However, as drying continued from the 75 per cent RH level to 50 per cent there was probably no further increase in the nonevaporable water. Therefore, the fire resistance of slabs at 75 per cent RH was lower than for slabs at 90 per cent RH because of the loss of evaporable water. This loss was offset somewhat by the dehydration of some of the chemically combined (non-evaporable) water during the fire test. Further shortening of the fire endurance time in the case of slabs dried to 50 per cent RH follows the further loss of evaporable water. The loss of evaporable water that resulted when the concrete RH was lowered from 75 to 50 per cent must have been quite appreciable to have reduced the fire endurance time of the slab by an additional 18 min.

Kiln Drying Without Controlled Humidity:

Note in Table 3 that at an ambient RH of 35 per cent approximately four months were required to dry, by natural means, a 6-in. concrete slab to a mid-thickness RH of 75 per cent. Lowering the ambient RH from 35 to 10 per cent reduced the natural drying time by one month. Three or even four months does not appear to be an excessively long period for drying concrete for the fire test. However, note that the slabs used in this study were dried under the following conditions: (1) The concrete had a water-cement ratio of 0.6, (2) Drying took place from both surfaces, (3) The specimens had a half thickness of only 3 in., and (4) The concrete was exposed to the drying environment after only seven days of fog-room curing. A reduction of the water-cement ratio or an increase in thickness or initial curing period could have doubled, and possibly tripled, the drying time neces-

sary to lower the concrete RH to the stated test level. For example, a 6-in. slab from another study of a similar concrete mix, but with a water-cement ratio of 0.45, required nearly eight months of natural drying at a relative humidity of 35 per cent to reach the 75 per cent RH level at the midthickness. Also, the effects on the humidity distribution of increasing the section depth were investigated by Ali and Kesler (12). They showed that the RH at the center in a 6 by 12 in. mortar cylinder was reduced to 90 per cent in 80 days. For the same storage time the RH at the center of a 12 by 12 in. cylinder of the same mix was 97 per cent. Thus, lengthy drying times preliminary to the fire test can occur, depending on the quality of the concrete and the thickness of the section. The need to accelerate the drying process is evident.

Information regarding the RH through slab sections and the drying periods required to reach the test RH at the middepths of the sections, when the slabs were dried artificially at 200 F without humidity control, is shown in Fig. 10. Also shown, for purposes of comparison, are the results from companion slabs which were naturally dried in air at 73 F and 35 per cent RH.

Humidity gradients and drying time— Actual relative humidities existing in the drying kilns, when operated at 200 F without special humidity control, were very low. Hygrometer measurements showed that they never exceeded 4 per cent. Since the air within the kilns was changed frequently, the kiln humidity was due to the relatively small quantity of moisture supplied by the specimens and that contained in the makeup air from the laboratory. Psychrometric data (13) indicate that when air at an RH of 70 per cent and temperature of 80 F is heated to 200 F it will register a RH of about 4 per cent.

Figure 10 shows that the length of time required to lower the concrete humidity in 6-in. slabs to test levels of 75 and 50 per cent RH was drastically reduced by simple artificial drying without kiln humidity control. The humidity gradients in the outer $\frac{3}{4}$-in. layer of the section were assumed. Only nine days in the heated kiln and 14 days under infrared heat radiation were required to realize 75 per cent RH at the midthickness of the slab as compared with 114 days for natural drying in air at 35 per cent RH and 73 F. The time savings afforded by artificial drying to the concrete test humidity of 50 per cent was much more pronounced. To realize this humidity condition in the slabs by natural drying, 850 days were required but only 25 and 36 days were needed, respectively, in the closed kiln and under infrared heat radiation. There is a slight difference in the gradients for the two methods of artificial drying to the 75 per cent test level, but at the 50 per cent test level the humidity gradients through slabs dried by the two methods were similar so that a single curve was drawn to represent them. The factor having the greatest influence, perhaps, on the drying time requirements was the velocity of the air over the specimens. Within the infrared heat radiation enclosure all air movement over the specimens was due to natural convection. The air velocity here was of the order of 0.5 ft/sec. The air was circulated within the kiln by means of several fans which produced an average air velocity of 2.5 ft/sec.

Figure 10 also shows that the RH gradient is highly dependent upon the manner in which the concrete is dried and the extent of the drying.

Fire endurance—The more steeply sloping RH curves produced by the two accelerated drying methods indicate that the amount of evaporable water

within the concretes had been reduced substantially below that retained by the concretes of the naturally dried slabs. It seems reaonable to expect, therefore, that the observed fire endurances of artificially dried slabs, as gaged by the unexposed surface temperature criteria, would also be lower than the standard fire endurances of naturally dried slabs. Fire endurance data relating to slabs which were kiln dried without humidity control, and to naturally dried companion slabs, are given in Table 5. The test results show that nearly equal fire endurances were obtained for slabs that were artificially dried, whether the drying was carried out in the heated air

TABLE 5—EFFECT OF DRYING PROCEDURE ON FIRE ENDURANCE.

Drying Procedure	Fire Endurance, min	
	75% RH	50% RH
Natural drying at 35 per cent RH, 73 F................	186	168
Kiln drying at 200 F........	166	151
Infrared radiation drying at 200 F..................	165	149

kiln or accomplished by exposure to infrared heat radiation. This was true for both the 75 and 50 per cent test levels. This similarity was anticipated because the humidity gradients produced by the two artificial drying methods were so alike. Unfortunately, artificial drying to the 75 per cent RH test level produced fire endurances that were 20 min less than the 186 min obtained for the specimen that was naturally dried to 75 per cent RH. Considering slabs dried to the 50 per cent RH level, the fire endurance of 168 min, which resulted for the naturally dried slab was reduced by 18 min to about 150 min. It is also interesting to note that a reduction of from 15 to 18 min in fire endurance was obtained for slabs either artificially or naturally dried when the test RH was lowered from 75 to 50 per cent. If it can be assumed that fire endurance, gaged in terms of heat transmission, is closely related to the evaporable water content of the concrete

per cent RH middepth level contained less evaporable water than that tested at 75 per cent RH, and (3) In drying concrete from the 75 to the 50 per cent RH test level approximately the same

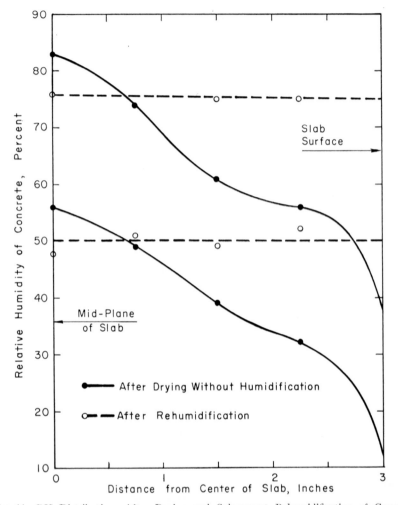

FIG. 11—RH Distributions After Drying and Subsequent Rehumidification of Concrete.

at time of the fire test, then these reduced fire resistances can be interpreted to indicate that: (1) Considerably more evaporable water was removed from the concrete by the artificial drying procedure than by the natural drying procedure, (2) Concrete tested at the 50

amount of evaporable water is lost whether natural drying or artificial drying at 200 F is applied.

Drying With Subsequent Rehumidification:

Kiln drying without humidity control

followed by rehumidification—Some test slabs which were conditioned in this manner were first dried in the heated air kiln, as described, to a middepth concrete RH of from 5 to 8 percentage points above the required test level. Seven days were required to reach the 75 per cent RH test level and 16 days for a 50 per cent RH level. The slabs were then rehumidified according to the schedule in Table 2.

Relative humidities through the sections after the initial drying and rehumidification periods for both test levels are shown in Fig. 11. The humidity gradients for the outer $\frac{3}{4}$ in. of the section were assumed. The gradients which resulted from drying without humidity control followed, generally, the gradients shown in Fig. 10 for the same type of drying. Further examination of the curves in Fig. 11 shows that the distributions obtained after the rehumidification period at 150 F and 75 or 50 per cent kiln RH were quite uniform. The final humidity gradients between middepth and the outer $\frac{3}{4}$-in., obtained after the rehumidification treatment, exhibit a uniformity like those obtained under natural drying at 35 per cent RH and 73 F.

If it is assumed that the quantity of evaporable water in the concrete of the test slab can be uniquely defined by its RH then the rehumidified slabs might be expected to have fire endurances similar to those which were naturally dried. The fire test results did not confirm this assumption. In fact, the fire endurance times for the rehumidified slabs were only 4 to 5 min longer than for those kiln dried without rehumidification. At the 75 per cent RH test level a fire endurance time of 169 min was obtained for the rehumidified concrete as compared with 165 min for the concrete artificially dried at 200 F in the kiln without humidity control.

This compares with the standard fire endurance of 186 min for the companion, naturally dried slab. At the 50 per cent RH test level the increase in fire endurance was only 5 min—from 150 to 155 min. This may be compared with the 168-min endurance time for the companion, naturally dried slab. Thus, it would seem that partial rehumidification of the concrete following artificial drying, in the manner described, does not offer much promise for simulat-

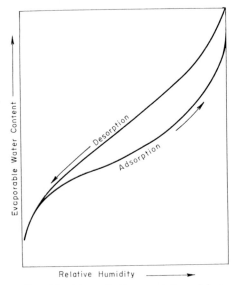

Fig. 12—Schematic Representation of Sorption Cycle.

ing the moisture condition and the fire endurance which results from natural drying in air at 73 F and 35 per cent RH.

An explanation for the reduced fire endurances which accompanied artificial drying in these experiments is complicated by the varying conditions of temperature and humidity that were employed. Basically, the drying-rehumidifying conditioning method involves fundamental sorption behavior—desorption during kiln drying and adsorption during the exposure to the high humidity of the rehumidifying treatment. Adsorption is

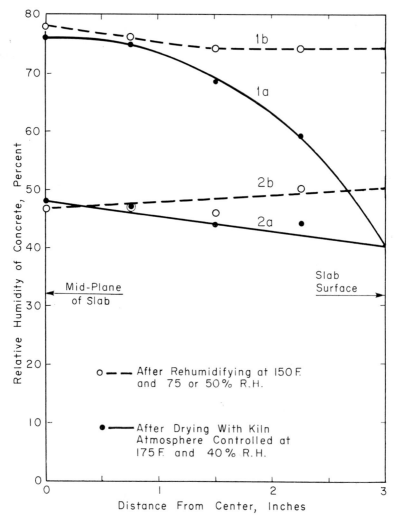

Fig. 13—Humidity Gradients Within Slabs Dried and Rehumidified Under Controlled Temperature and Humidity.

defined as the gain of moisture from the ambient atmosphere; desorption, the loss of moisture to the atmosphere. The curves used to represent these processes are called isotherms and show the relationships between water content and relative vapor pressures (RH) at constant temperatures. A sorption cycle is shown schematically in Fig. 12. A significant characteristic of the cycle

is that moisture which is lost during the first drying phase cannot be completely replaced through adsorption, except at very low relative vapor pressures. Thus, for the same RH the concrete has a lower actual moisture content at the end of the adsorption process than during the desorption phase of the cycle. This phenomenon is called sorption hysteresis.

Sorption isotherms for concrete of the

quality employed in this study were not obtained. However, it appears that the amount of evaporable water that may be lost in the sorption cycle can be substantial. Powers and Brownyard (10) reported that for a hardened cement paste of 0.5 water-cement ratio and $7\frac{1}{2}$-year old, approximately 25 per cent of the evaporable water was lost due to sorption hysteresis at a relative vapor pressure of 75 per cent. Also, Jesser (14) found that a hardened cement paste

evaporable water, normally available in naturally dried concrete, was not present here, even though the concrete humidity gradients, except near the surface, compared very favorably with those of naturally dried slabs.

The results of this drying procedure also showed that RH alone is not a positive gage of moisture content in concrete.

Drying with controlled humidity followed by rehumidification—For the fourth

TABLE 6—SUMMARY OF FIRE TESTS OF SIX-INCH CONCRETE SLABS.

Conditioning Treatment	Fire Endurance Time at Maximum Concrete RH Shown, min[a]		
	90%	75%	50%
Natural drying:			
73 F and 10 per cent RH......................	194	188	165
73 F and 35 per cent RH......................	192	186[b]	168
73 F and 50 per cent RH......................	189	184	...
73 F and 75 per cent RH......................	192	...	...
Kiln drying:			
200 F, no humidity control....................	...	166	151
200 F, infrared heat radiation.................	...	165	149
200 F followed by rehumidification (per schedule Table 2)..	...	169	155
175 F and 40 per cent RH followed by rehumidification in kiln atmosphere at 150 F and 75 or 50 per cent RH...............................	...	170	156

[a] Based on time for average unexposed surface temperature to rise 250 F above the initial surface temperature, or the unexposed surface temperature at any one point of measurement to rise 325 F above the initial surface temperature, whichever occurs first. In each of these tests the average temperature rise of 250 F occurred first.

[b] Standard fire endurance.

of very low water-cement ratio, cured in water for three days, lost more than 60 per cent of the evaporable water during a sorption cycle at the 75 per cent relative vapor pressure level. In both of the above cases substantial additional amounts of evaporable water were lost at the 50 per cent RH vapor pressure level. It seems likely, therefore, that sorption hysteresis played an important role in preventing an adequate regain of moisture by the test slabs that were artificially dried and subsequently rehumidified. The reduced fire endurances of these slabs indicated that considerable

accelerated drying method the kiln humidity was controlled from the start of the drying cycle. The objective here was to lower the RH within the concrete slab more gradually so that the moisture gradient would be minimized. If the moisture gradient could be maintained reasonably uniform through the section during the drying process, the hysteresis effect upon rehumidification would also be minimized.

Humidity gradients obtained by drying at 175 F and 40 per cent RH (kiln atmosphere), followed by rehumidification at 150 F and 75 or 50 per cent RH are shown in Fig. 13. Gradients in the outer $\frac{3}{4}$ in. of sections are assumed. Thirteen days for the drying phase and five days for the rehumidifying phase were required at the test level of 75 per cent RH. At the test level of 50 per cent RH, 26 and four days were respectively taken up by the drying and rehumidifying phases of the conditioning treatment. For both test humidity levels less water seems to have been removed from the concrete when the drying was conducted with some controlled kiln humidity. Nevertheless, the resulting fire endurances did not bear this out. In Table 6 these apparent fire endurances are compared with the results of all fire tests that were conducted in the investigation. It will be seen that from the practical viewpoint accelerated drying at the indicated temperatures produced an approximately common result, irrespective of variations in the kiln humidity.

SUMMARY AND CONCLUSIONS

This investigation was designed to provide needed information relative to the effects on the standard fire endurance of the conditioning method which may be used to prepare concrete slab specimens for the standard fire test. The program did not include all of the possible methods, but it is believed that those used were the simplest and most economical. The results are applicable only to slabs and under the conditions of drying described. Laboratory pilot tests and information from the literature indicate that these results may be modified in varying degrees by a number of factors. Some of these are mass and shape of the specimen, design of the concrete mix, type of aggregate, age before the exposure to the conditioning or drying procedure, temperature and humidity levels of the conditioning environment, and physico-chemical changes due to the drying procedure.

The results of the present program indicate:

1. Although lowering the environmental RH to 10 per cent under the natural drying procedure accelerated the drying of the concrete at all middepth test levels, nearly two years was still required to lower the concrete RH at the midthickness to 50 per cent.

2. The humidity distribution within concrete slabs resulting from the natural drying procedure for the 90 and 75 per cent RH test levels was practically independent of the ambient RH. Humidity measurements indicated a uniform distribution of moisture within the section except for the outer $\frac{3}{4}$ in. zone.

3. At each of the three RH test levels (90, 75, and 50 per cent) the environmental humidity employed in the natural drying process had little influence on the fire endurances obtained for each test level.

4. Drying at 200 F in either the closed, heated air kiln or in the infrared heat radiation enclosure reduced markedly the time to reach the test level.

5. Significantly lower RH distributions were produced in concrete dried at 200 F than in concretes naturally dried to the same middepth RH. They indicated that the concrete was quite dry except for a narrow zone at middepth.

6. The apparent fire endurances obtained for slabs dried at 200 F were substantially lower than those for naturally dried slabs. The standard fire endurance time of a slab naturally dried to 75 per cent RH at middepth was 37 min greater than a companion slab artificially dried at 200 F to 50 per cent RH.

7. Rehumidifying the slabs after artificial drying at elevated temperatures with or without controlled kiln humidity during the drying cycle produced a uniform RH within the concrete which approached that obtained by natural drying; however, the rehumidifying

processes had little effect on the fire resistance.

8. Sorption hystersis had an important influence in the apparently reduced fire resistances of concrete slabs that were dried and rehumidified.

9. The fact that RH does not uniquely define the moisture content of the concrete was substantiated by results of fire tests on artificially dried slabs.

10. All of the artificial drying methods employed resulted in substantial savings in the time required to condition the slabs to a specified internal RH, but produced substantially lower apparent fire endurances.

11. When artificial drying is employed, the application of a compensatory adjustment to the apparent fire endurance seems justified.

REFERENCES

(1) C. C. Carlson, "Fire Resistance of Prestressed Concrete Beams. Study A—Influence of Thickness of Concrete Covering over Prestressing Steel Strand," *Bulletin 147*, Research Dept., Portland Cement Assn., Chicago, Ill., 1959.

(2) S. L. Selvaggio and C. C. Carlson, "Effect of Restraint on the Fire Resistance of Prestressed Concrete," *Symposium on Fire Test Methods, ASTM STP 344*, Am. Soc. Testing Mats., 1962, p. 91; *Bulletin 164*, Research Dept., Portland Cement Assn., Chicago, Ill.

(3) S. L. Selvaggio and C. C. Carlson, "Fire Resistance of Prestressed Concrete Beams. Study B—Influence of Aggregate and Load Intensity," *Journal*, Portland Cement Assn., Research and Development Laboratories, Vol. 6, No. 1, Jan., 1964, pp. 41–64; Vol. 6, No. 2, May, 1964.

(4) L. A. Ashton and S. C. C. Bate, "The Fire Resistance of Prestressed Concrete Beams," *Paper 6444*, The Institution of Civil Engrs., London, 1960; *Journal*, Am. Concrete Inst., May, 1961, p. 1417.

(5) C. A. Menzel, "A Method for Determining the Moisture Condition of Hardened Concrete in Terms of Relative Humidity," *Proceedings*, Am. Soc. Testing Mats., Vol. 55, 1955, p. 1085.

(6) G. E. Monfore, "A Small Probe Type Gage for Measuring Relative Humidity," *Bulletin 160*, Research Dept., Portland Cement Assn., Chicago, Ill.; Reprinted, *Journal*, Portland Cement Assn., Research and Development Laboratories, Vol. 5, No. 2, May, 1963, pp. 23–26.

(7) J. C. Saeman and G. W. Washa, "Variation of Mortar and Concrete Properties with Temperature," *Journal*, Am. Concrete Inst., Vol. 29, No. 5, Nov., 1957, pp. 385–395; *Proceedings 54*.

(8) H. Matthieu, "Behavior of Concrete at 80 to 300 C," *BETON Herstellung Verwendung*, Vol. 12, No. 8, Aug., 1962, pp. 363–364.

(9) M. S. Abrams, "Surface Temperature Measurements with Felted Asbestos Pads," *Bulletin 137*, Research Dept., Portland Cement Assn., Chicago, Ill., 1962; Reprinted *Journal*, Portland Cement Assn., Research and Development Laboratories, Vol. 4, No. 1, 1962, pp. 22–30.

(10) T. C. Powers and T. L. Brownyard, "Studies of the Physical Properties of Hardened Portland Cement Paste," *Proceedings*, Am. Concrete Inst., Vol. 43, 1947; *Bulletin 22*, Research Dept., Portland Cement Assn., Chicago, Ill., 1948.

(11) F. M. Lea and C. H. Desch, *The Chemistry of Cement and Concrete*, Edwards Arnolds, Ltd., London, 1956.

(12) I. Ali and C. E. Kesler, "Creep in Concrete with and without Exchange of Moisture with the Environment," *T. and A. M. Report 641*, Department of Theoretical and Applied Mechanics, University of Illinois, 1963.

(13) H. H. Smith, "Relative Humidity and Equilibrium Moisture Content Graphs and Tables for Use in Kiln Drying Lumber," *Report 1651*, Forest Products Laboratory, Forest Service, U. S. Department of Agriculture, May, 1956.

(14) Leopold Jesser, *Zement*, Vol. 16, 1927, p. 741.

DISCUSSION

C. L. Pettibone[1]—Has research been done on the drying methods for hollow-core precast floor and roof slabs, and the effects of drying on the endpoint reading of heat transmission in ASTM Method E 119? Is any research in process or contemplated on the drying method planned for the future on prestress, precast floor and roof slabs?

M. S. Abrams and D. L. Orals (*authors*)—No research has been done on drying methods for hollow-core units at the Portland Cement Association Laboratories. However, a research program on hollow-core slabs which will be naturally dried is being planned. The drying of these units is not expected to exceed four months, since the distance to the deepest part of the concrete from a drying surface is of the order of a few inches.

The drying of hollow-core units by artificial means which would reduce the moisture content of the concrete would reduce the fire endurance. Also, the drier concrete cover over the steel would allow the steel to reach higher temperatures earlier in the fire test than in naturally dried concrete. This might result in less favorable structural performance for the artificially dried units.

Some work is just getting underway on precast, prestressed, double-tee concrete units. Some of the members will be naturally dried, while others will be dried by artificial means.

Daniel Gross[2]—With respect to the sorption hysteresis characteristics of concrete, what effect would adsorption-desorption cycling due to seasonal changes in ambient RH be expected to have on the fire endurance of concrete structures in service?

Mr. Abrams and Mr. Orals—We have not been able to find extensive information regarding Mr. Gross's inquiry on the effect of adsorption-desorption cycling due to seasonal changes in ambient RH on the fire endurance of concrete structures in service. There are, however, some complicated aspects to this question. The effect of each sorption cycle on the amount of moisture in the concrete would depend on the previous cycles experienced by the material. The initial curing procedure of the concrete would also affect all subsequent sorption cycles. Also to be considered is the depth to which the sorption cycle affects the moisture condition of the concrete. Concrete of low permeability may experience changes in moisture due to the adsorption-desorption phenomena, only near the surface. The effect on the moisture condition of more porous masonry units could be more pronounced and extend well into the depth of the unit.

Work is presently underway to determine sorption-cycle effect on the moisture content of concrete in service. This is being done by installing humidity-measuring equipment in hardened concrete structures within and without the concrete of the laboratory buildings. Perhaps this work can be extended to include specimens which can be readily tested by exposure to the standard fire test.

[1] Executive secretary, Flexicore Manufacturer's Assn., Columbus, Ohio.
[2] Physicist, National Bureau of Standards Washington, D. C.

H. J. Roux[3]—The content of this paper is very important to those involved with the design and testing of fire resistant ceilings as part of time design-rated assemblies which include concrete slabs. Is any information available regarding the natural drying time of various thickness slabs, or those where one surface of the slab is sealed (by a metal deck, for example)?

MR. ABRAMS AND MR. ORALS—Information is presently being obtained on the natural drying time for 3 by 3-ft concrete slabs, 5, 6, and 7 in. thick. This information will be available in three or four months. Only an approximate reply can be given to the other part of Mr. Roux's question. For very thin slabs (up to about 3 in.) sealed on one side, the drying time should be nearly equal to that of a slab of twice the thickness, drying from both sides. However, as the thickness increases the concrete drying from one side would probably take a longer period of time than the concrete of twice the thickness drying from both sides.

---

[3] Manager, ceilings systems research, Armstrong Cork Co., Lancaster, Pa.

EFFECT OF MOISTURE ON THE FIRE ENDURANCE OF BUILDING ELEMENTS[1]

By T. Z. Harmathy[2]

Synopsis

The effect of moisture on the performance of building elements in fire is closely related to the amount of moisture, and in turn, to the sorption characteristics of materials.

High moisture content may result in spalling. The probable mechanism of moisture clog spalling is discussed, and a criterion is developed for the fractional pore saturation at which spalling can be expected (Eq 8).

If spalling does not occur, the presence of moisture is beneficial for the fire endurance. An empirical equation has been found which correlates the percentage gain in fire endurance due to 1 per cent moisture with the fire endurance in the dry condition (Eq 20). A nomogram is presented to facilitate estimation of the effect of moisture on thermal fire endurance (Fig. 9).

Possible utilization of the results in the field of fire endurance testing is discussed.

The realization that the moisture inevitably present in almost any building material may have a marked effect on the performance of building elements in fire, and may present a serious problem in the reproducibility of the results of standard fire tests, prompted a significant revision of ASTM Method E 119[3] in 1959. So significant was this revision that, if enforced retrospectively, it would have invalidated hundreds of fire test results.

Although this revision helped in calling attention to the fact that such problems exist, the solution offered by it cannot be regarded as more than temporary.

If the effect of a variable on the result of some test is clearly proved, but not known quantitatively, the correct attitude is to face the problem by studying the relation between the cause and effect. One may seemingly dispose of that variable by prescribing it a constant value during the test, but further unexpected problems may arise while the basic problem remains unanswered.

Some problems coming in the wake of setting an upper limit to the equilibrium relative humidity[4] of fire test specimens are already seen clearly, others have so far remained unnoticed. Frequent questions include: Should the upper limit be 75, 70, or 50 per cent? Can forced drying be permitted and under what conditions? Will a specimen that satisfies such mois-

[1] Although this paper deals with brick and concrete walls only, most of the conclusions are applicable to other types of building materials.

[2] Research officer, Fire Research Section, Division of Building Research, National Research Council, Ottawa, Canada.

[3] Methods of Fire Tests of Building Construction and Materials (E 119), *1964 Book of ASTM Standards*, Part 14.

[4] Equilibrium relative humidity is an abbreviated term meaning equilibrium pressure of water vapor in the pores of solid, expressed as relative humidity.

ture requirements also satisfy the more basic requirement that a specimen must be representative of what the actual construction is in service?

It is impossible to find valid answers

librium relative humidity. Some materials can be forced-dried at very high temperatures, others change significantly in their characteristic features if subjected to drying at an early stage.

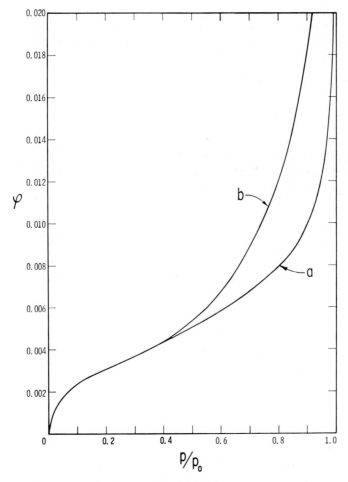

FIG. 1—Calculated Sorption Isotherms of a Certain Clay Brick.
(a) Adsorption Branch
(b) Desorption Branch

for all circumstances. Some materials can be tested at high equilibrium relative humidities without any noticeable effect from the presence of moisture. Others will yield markedly different performances even at 5 per cent change in the equi-

For some building elements, those to be erected in dry areas or where the heating season is long, the representative moisture content may be much less than that in equilibrium with 50 per cent relative humidity (RH). In some other cases, because of specific service conditions, an average equilibrium RH higher than 75 per cent may be anticipated.

It is obvious that none of these problems would arise if the effect of moisture on the fire endurance were known. Test specimens could be subjected to fire tests at any (or almost any) moisture content; thus, the time devoted to conditioning could serve a very useful purpose—that of attaining the physical properties characteristic of the material under actual service conditions.

This paper presents the results of investigations into the effect of moisture on the fire endurance of building elements. The possible utilization of the results in the field of fire endurance testing will be discussed in the last section.

Sorption Characteristics of Building Materials

The effect of moisture on the fire endurance of building elements is, of course, closely related to the amount of moisture, and, in turn, to the sorption characteristics of materials. The basic laws governing the adsorption of moisture, or *adsorbate*, in general, by a porous solid (*adsorbent*) are discussed by Sereda and Hutcheon.[5] They note that the amount of moisture held by a solid at various vapor pressures, in other words, the shape of sorption isotherms, depends on the specific surface, the effective porosity, and the pore geometry (basic pore shape, pore size distribution, etc.) of the solid, and that in the domain of capillary condensation marked sorption hysteresis can be experienced.

Although these sorption characteristics can be determined from relatively simple experiments (1),[6] it is often desirable to have an estimate of them.

Harmathy, in another paper (2), shows how the basic laws of adsorption and some experimental data can be used to estimate the moisture sorption isotherms and isosteres of building materials.

Figure 1 shows the moisture sorption isotherms of a certain type of clay brick, obtained by calculations. The shape of the curves can be regarded as typical of building materials in general, with the important exception of concrete. In the case of concrete, the hysteresis loop extends to the whole $0 < p < p_0$ pressure range.[7] To understand the cause of this unusual behavior one should realize that the binding energy for some water molecules held in the portland cement paste by chemical bonds is less than the energy needed to dislodge the most firmly held adsorbed molecules during drying. Consequently, at some advanced stage of drying, desorption and partial dehydration will take place simultaneously. Since the amount of water held by adsorption cannot be determined exactly, that part of water which is dislodged by some standard drying procedure is more accurately called evaporable water, rather than moisture. For similar reasons, the amount of water retained by the hydrated cement throughout the drying should be termed nonevaporable water.

Obviously, in the case of concrete, the reference state of the material is not its "dry" state, but a state determined by some standard drying procedure. Among the various drying techniques two are generally accepted as standard: (1) drying over ice at -78.5 C (sublimation temperature of CO_2), so-called D drying, and (2) drying in an oven at 105 C.

In the light of this discussion it seems most probable that the unusual shape of sorption isotherms of concrete is due to partial or complete rehydration, during adsorption, of the water of constitution

---

[5] See p. 3.

[6] The boldface numbers in parentheses refer to the list of references appended to this paper.

[7] Symbols are listed at the end of the paper.

lost at very low pressures during desorption.

The sorption characteristics of portland cement paste and concrete depend very strongly on the degree of hydration (1,3,4), and thus on the age, conditioning procedure, and some other factors. Under ordinary circumstances a sufficiently large mass of concrete can retain enough water in its pores to secure the progress of hydration for a very long peiiod after the removal of forms and protecting covers. If, however, the concrete is

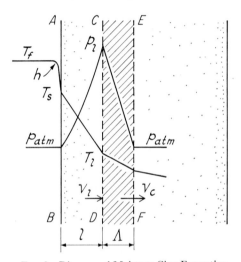

FIG. 2—Diagram of Moisture Clog Formation.

subjected to forced drying, the hydration slows down considerably as the RH in the pores becomes lower than 95 per cent, and stops completely at 80 per cent (5).

SPALLING

Because of the marked differences in the sorption characteristics of various building materials the amount of moisture that these materials hold at normal atmospheric conditions may be very significant in certain cases, or barely noticeable in others.

As already mentioned, the presence of

moisture is sometimes detrimental, sometimes beneficial. As for its detrimental effect, there is now sufficient evidence that excessive moisture is at least one of those factors which may cause violent spalling of concrete at some early stage of fire exposure.

The factors affecting the most common mode of spalling, the so-called thermal spalling, have been under scrutiny for several decades. It is generally accepted that increasing values of the group $\sigma_f(1 - \nu)/E\alpha$ indicate, at least approximately, an increasing resistance to thermal spalling. The $(1 - \nu)/E\alpha$ group always appears in expressions obtained for thermal stresses in solids, if the calculations are based on the assumptions that E, ν, and α are constant in the temperature range concerned, and the material is perfectly elastic. Such assumptions are obviously not applicable to concrete, which exhibits a mixed elastic-plastic behavior at any load even at room temperature and, owing to decomposition, often marked shrinkage instead of expansion upon heating. Because of these characteristics, concrete is rarely liable to thermal spalling.

A probable mechanism of spalling of concrete, called moisture clog spalling,[8] during fire exposure was described by Shorter and Harmathy (6) as follows. When heat begins to penetrate into a concrete slab, desorption of moisture starts in a thin layer adjoining the surface exposed to fire. A major portion of the released vapors leave toward the colder regions and become readsorbed in the pores of some neighboring layer. As

[8] The difference between thermal spalling and moisture clog spalling occurring during standard fire endurance tests is easily recognizable. Moisture clog spalling is generally more violent and the thickness of the dislodged layers is greater, about 1 in. Spalling of concrete may also be due to other factors, such as excessive deformation, expansion of reinforcing steel, or crystalline transformation in certain aggregates, especially those of high quartz content.

the thickness of the dry layer gradually increases, a completely saturated layer of considerable thickness (called a moisture clog here), builds up at some distance from the exposed surface. A little later, a sharply defined front forms between the dry and saturated layers (Fig. 2). Further desorption will obviously take place from this frontal area (indicated by Line CD).

In the meantime the temperature of the exposed surface keeps rising, and a very steep temperature gradient develops across the dry layer resulting in high heat flow and intensified desorption at the CD plane. Having little passage toward the colder regions, the vapors have to leave through the dry layer, gradually expanding and meeting increasing resistance along the flow path. With further steepening of the temperature gradient there will be a rapid pressure buildup at Plane CD.

If the resistance of the pores to moisture flow is not too high, under the effect of the developed large pressure difference, the moisture clog (Region $CDEF$) begins to move toward the colder regions and the pressure buildup soon levels off. If, on the other hand, the permeability of the material is low, the pressure at Plane CD continues to grow and will eventually exceed the ultimate tensile strength of the material. When this condition is reached, a layer of a thickness approximately equal to that of the dry layer separates from the material.

If this suggested mechanism is correct, one could expect that material properties, such as porosity, permeability, ultimate strength, and thermal conductivity (by affecting the heat flow through the dry layer) will appear in an expression, the value of which determines whether moisture clog spalling will take place at a given moisture content. Because of the very involved mechanism of combined heat and moisture flow, it is

unavoidable to base the derivation of such a criterion on a greatly simplified mathematical model, as follows.

Figure 2 is a schematic illustration of the conditions arising in a concrete slab exposed to fire at a stage when the formation of the dry layer and moisture clog is completed, and the desorption takes place from Frontal Plane CD. If it is assumed that a fraction δ of the moisture previously desorbed from Layer $ABCD$ has been readsorbed by Layer $CDEF$. The following relationship is obtained between Λ and l

$$\Lambda = \delta l \; \frac{\varphi}{\epsilon - \varphi} \dots\dots\dots\dots (1)$$

Assuming, furthermore, quasi-steady-state conditions within Region $ABCD$,[9] and applying heat balance to Surface AB, the surface temperature can be expressed as

$$T_s = \frac{T_l + (hl/k)T_f}{1 + (hl/k)} \dots\dots\dots (2)$$

and the heat flow as

$$q = \frac{h(T_f - T_l)}{1 + (hl/k)} \dots\dots\dots (3)$$

The rate at which Front CD recedes due to vaporization is[10]

$$v_l = \frac{q}{Q\rho_w\epsilon} \dots\dots\dots\dots (4)$$

The velocity of the moisture clog, Region $CDEF$, as a whole, can be expressed from Darcy's law

$$v_c = \frac{\kappa}{\eta} \frac{p_l - p_{\mathrm{atm}}}{\Lambda} \dots\dots\dots (5)$$

---

[9] This is a reasonable assumption. Observations and calculations indicate that within the period when spalling might occur (10 to 25 min in the case of standard fire tests), the variation rate of the average temperature of the Region $ABCD$ is not very significant.

[10] Effective porosity is the volume fraction permeable to the adsorbate (water) and is generally slightly less than the true porosity.

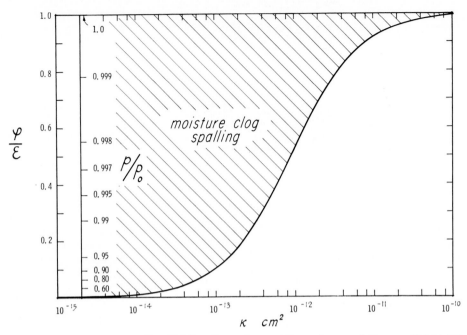

FIG. 3—Moisture Clog Spalling Liability Curve. Assumed Properties: $\epsilon = 0.30$, $\sigma_f = 17.0 \times 10^6$ dyne/cm², $k = 1.0 \times 10^{-2}$ J/cm sec deg K.

The condition $v_c > v_l$ can be interpreted that the moisture clog moves fast enough to prevent further pressure buildup at Plane CD. On the other hand, $v_c < v_l$ means that the moisture clog cannot yield to the pressure, and the pressure buildup continues owing to increasing rate of vaporization of Front CD. Thus, spalling will take place if

$$p_l - p_{\text{atm}} = \sigma_f \dots\dots\dots(6)$$

and

$$v_c < v_l \dots\dots\dots\dots(7)$$

By combining Eqs 1 and 3 to 6, with Inequality 7, the following criterion is obtained for the fractional pore saturation, φ/ϵ, at which disruption of the concrete slab is expected

$$\frac{\varphi}{\epsilon} > \frac{1}{1 + (A/\epsilon\kappa\sigma_f)[k/(k + B)]} \dots(8)$$

where

$$A \equiv \frac{\delta l \eta h (T_f - T_s)}{Q\rho_w} \dots\dots\dots(9)$$

and

$$B \equiv hl \dots\dots\dots\dots(10)$$

and both are considered approximately constant. After assigning plausible values to δ, l, η, etc. in Eqs 9 and 10

$$A = 2.1 \times 10^{-5} \text{ dyne}$$

$$B = 3.6 \times 10^{-2} \text{ J/cm sec deg K}$$

or, if one prefers substituting κ in darcies, σ_f in psi, and k in Btu/ft hr deg F

$$A = 0.031 \text{ darcies in.}^2/\text{lb}$$

$$B = 2.1 \text{ Btu/ft hr deg F}$$

Figure 3 shows the variation of allowable fractional pore saturation with permeability, calculated by using Eq 8 with $\epsilon = 0.30$, $\sigma_f = 17 \times 10^6$ dyne/cm² (250 psi) and $k = 10^{-2}$ J/cm sec deg K

TABLE 1—MATERIALS AND GEOMETRIES STUDIED FOR DETERMINING THE EXPLICIT FORM OF EQ 12.

No.	Material	Composition, % by weight	Nature of Study	Properties of Material Plotted in	Moisture Content, per cent by volume	Geometries[a]
1	Concrete 1 (assumed)	15.6 hpc[b] 84.4 quartz gravel	computer calculations	Fig. 4a	0 4.0 8.0	S-3⅝, S-5⅝, S-7⅞, H-7¾–83.3, H-7¾–77.8, H-7¾–71.4, H-7¾–55.6
2	Concrete 2 (assumed)	15.4 hpc 84.6 anorthosite rock	computer calculations	Fig. 4b	0 4.0 8.0	S-3⅝, S-5⅝, S-7⅞, H-7¾–83.3, H-7¾–77.8, H-7¾–71.4, H-7¾–55.6
3	Concrete 3 (assumed)	25.3 hpc 74.7 expanded shale	computer calculations	Fig. 5a	0 4.0 8.0	S-3⅝, S-5⅝, S-7⅞, H-7¾–77.8, H-7¾–71.4, H-7¾–55.6
4	Concrete 4 (assumed)	19.6 hpc 80.4 expanded shale	computer calculations	Fig. 5b	0 4.0 8.0	S-3⅝, S-5⅝, S-7⅞, H-7¾–77.8, H-7¾–71.4, H-7¾–55.6
5	Concrete 5 (existing)	17.5 hpc 82.5 expanded shale	fire endurance tests	Fig. 6b	0 to 20.8	S-3⅝, H-5⅝–89.1, H-5⅝–68.8
6	Brown clay brick (existing)	...	computer calculations and fire endurance tests	Fig. 6a	0 to 21.8	S-2½, S-4, S-6, S-8[c]
7	Insulating fire brick (existing)	...	fire endurance tests	Fig. 6b	0 to 9.9	H-8¼–46.7

[a] S-3⅝ means solid wall of 3⅝ in. thickness.
H-7¾–83.3 means hollow wall of 7¾ in. over-all thickness and 83.3 per cent solid.
[b] Hydrated portland cement.
[c] Computer calculations only.

(0.578 Btu/ft hr deg F). If one knows the sorption isotherms of the concrete, the scale on the vertical axis can be changed to read RH instead of fractional pore saturation. In Fig. 3 the desorption branch of the isotherm shown in Fig. 1 was used to illustrate how the transformation of scale is done. (Obviously, the adsorption branch should be used when equilibrium conditions are attained by wetting instead of drying.)

According to Fig. 3, moisture clog spalling is not likely to happen even at complete pore saturation if the permeability of the material is higher than about 5×10^{-11} cm^2 (0.005 darcies). Although this value seems to be within the expected range, it should be remembered that at present no experimental proofs are yet available for the confirmation of the validity of Eq 8.

In the case of bricks, the permeability is rarely lower than 0.005 darcies, thus moisture clog spalling is very unlikely. A recent series of experiments seemed to support this conclusion. It was also found, however, that brick constructions are often liable to thermal spalling.

It may be noticed that the permeability of mature portland cement pastes is several orders of magnitude lower than that of fresh pastes (3,7); thus, with aging concretes become more vulnerable to moisture clog spalling.

GAIN IN THERMAL FIRE ENDURANCE

If spalling is not expected to take place, the presence of moisture in building materials is beneficial for fire endurance. The primary reason is obvious: The absorption of heat associated with the desorption of moisture checks the rise of temperature in a building element during fire exposure, delaying the development of various undesirable phenomena which eventually lead to the failure of the building element.

Since, directly or indirectly, it is always the rise of temperature that causes the failure of a construction, the thermal performance of a building element, expressed in a conveniently defined unit (in terms of thermal fire endurance)[11] is generally a reliable measure of its overall performance in fire. Thus a figure of merit, expressing the beneficial effect of moisture on the performance of a construction, can be defined by

$$\psi = \frac{\tau_\varphi - \tau_d}{\tau_d \varphi} \dots\dots\dots(11)$$

This figure of merit of moisture expresses the percentage increase in thermal fire endurance in relation to the percentage (by volume) moisture content. Previous theoretical studies (8) indicated that for a given material and geometry of construction $(\tau_\varphi - \tau_d)/\tau_d$ is approximately proportional to φ, thus, in general

$$\psi = f \text{ (properties of materials, geometry)} \dots(12)$$

but is independent of φ.

To determine the explicit form of Eq 12, 90 computer calculations and 49 fire endurance tests have been performed. The materials and geometries studied are summarized in Table 1.

Concretes 1 to 4 are assumed materials. Each was selected to represent an extreme case in the group of either dense or lightweight concretes. Since quartz is the best and anorthosite probably the poorest thermal conductor among natural rocks used as aggregates, the thermal fire endurance yielded by Concrete 1 can be regarded as the lowest, and that yielded by Concrete 2 as the highest obtainable at a given geometry with dense concretes. Similarly, the properties of Concretes 3 and 4 were selected in such a way that no lightweight (nonautoclaved) concrete is expected to

[11] The thermal fire endurance is the time at which the average temperature on one side of a construction exceeds its initial value by 139 C, when the other side is exposed to a standard fire specified by ASTM Method E 119.

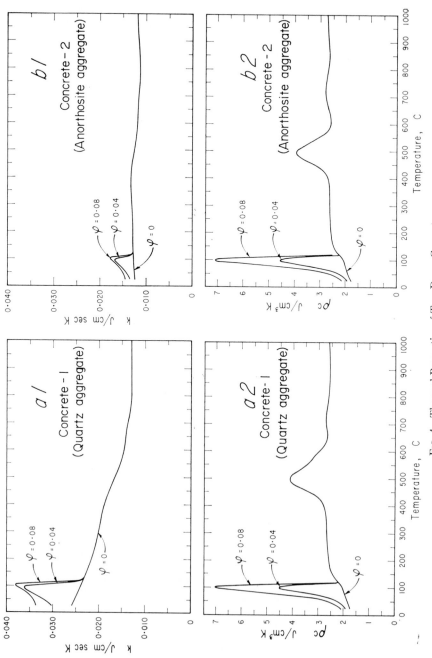

Fig. 4—Thermal Properties of Two Dense Concretes.

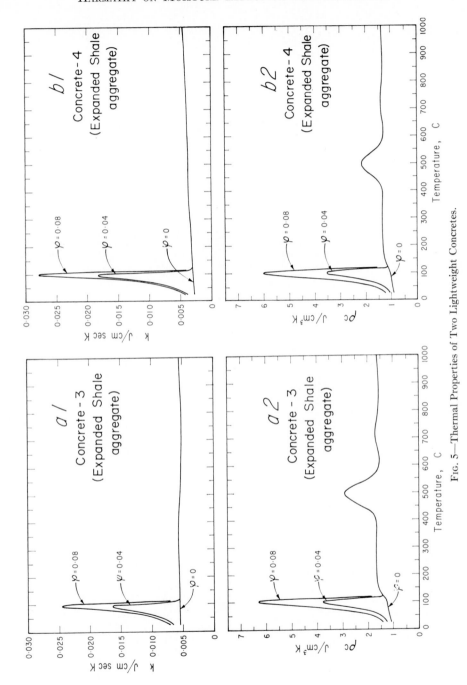

FIG. 5—Thermal Properties of Two Lightweight Concretes.

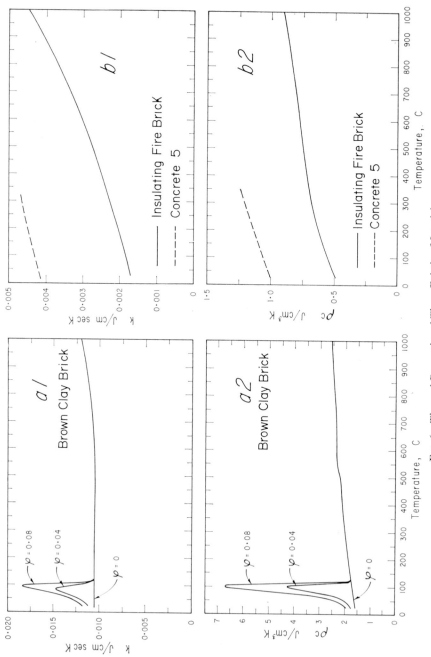

Fig. 6—Thermal Properties of Three Existing Materials.

yield lower thermal fire endurance than Concrete 3, or higher fire endurance than Concrete 4. The thermal conductivity versus temperature, and heat capacity versus temperature[12] curves for these materials (Figs. 4 and 5) are naturally theoretical curves, yet based on numerous experimental results and thermodynamic data concerning the constituent materials. The methods of calculation will be reported elsewhere.

The k versus temperature and ρc versus temperature cruves for Concrete

versus T, and ρc versus T curves corrected for the presence of moisture, could lead to strictly correct results only in the case of such fictitious solids which have zero permeability in the direction of heat flow and infinite permeability perpendicular to the heat flow. In such hypothetical solids neither moisture (adsorbate) nor vapor could migrate along or opposite to the direction of heat flow, and the desorbed vapors could leave the solid infinitely fast along isothermal surfaces. Real solids, of course, have finite

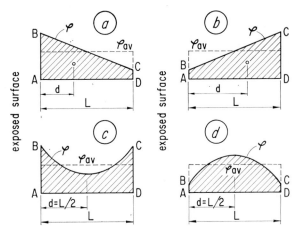

FIG. 7—Elucidation of Rule of Moisture Moment.

5, Brown Clay Brick, and Insulating Fire Brick, are entirely or principally experimental curves, determined by means of a variable-state method (9).

In all figures the curve sections representing 4 and 8 per cent (by volume) moisture content have been obtained by calculations. The effect of moisture on the thermal conductivity has been evaluated by using a somewhat modified form of Krischer's theory (10).

It should be emphasized that fire endurance calculations based on such k

permeability in all directions, and since under conditions arising during fire exposure, the paths representing the least resistance to fluid flow and the heat flow lines are generally coincident, one can expect marked moisture and vapor migration both along and opposite to the heat flow. As mentioned earlier, the following types of mass migration are conceivable: (1) migration of desorbed vapor in the direction opposite to the heat flow, primarily under the effect of pressure gradient, (2) apparent moisture (adsorbate) migration in the direction of heat flow by desorption-resorption sequence, induced by gradients of pressure and of vapor concentration, (3) moisture

---

[12] Note that in these graphs ρc should be interpreted as total heat capacity, obtained as the tangent to the volumetric enthalpy versus temperature curve (8).

(adsorbate) migration in the direction of heat flow under the effect of pressure gradient.

To learn about the probable effect of these migrations on heat transfer, a series of numerical analyses was undertaken to determine the thermal fire endurance of four $3\frac{3}{4}$-in. brick walls, all containing 5.3 per cent (by volume) moisture, but distributed over the thickness in different ways. The results indicated that the moisture distribution had a very significant effect on the thermal fire endurance. It was found that the increase in fire endurance was proportional, not to the moisture content, but to its moment about the surface exposed to fire.

This finding, which may be called the rule of moisture moment, is an extremely useful tool of theoretical fire endurance rating. Its application to practical problems is illustrated in Fig. 7 where four different moisture distributions across a wall of thickness L are shown. In all four cases, the average moisture content is the same, in other words, Areas $ABCD$ are identical. As stated by the rule of moisture moment, the gain in fire endurance is proportional to the product of Area $ABCD$ and the distance of the center of gravity of this area from the exposed surface d. It is now easy to see that the fire endurance corresponding to a distribution shown in Fig. 7a will be less than that corresponding to a distribution shown in Fig. 7b. On the other hand, if the moisture distribution is symmetrical about the center line, as in the cases shown in Figs. 7c and 7d, the distance of the center of gravity of Areas $ABCD$ from the exposed surface is always equal to the half thickness of the wall; thus, if Areas $ABCD$ are equal, equal fire endurances will result.

With the conventional conditioning procedures the symmetry of moisture distribution in wall fire test specimens is always ensured, thus, the result of the

fire test is expected to depend on the average moisture content only, and to be independent of the moisture distribution.

It is now possible to evaluate the effect of the three types of mass flow on the thermal fire endurance. In the case of Type 1 flow the desorbed vapors proceed toward hotter layers, absorb sensible heat, and hinder the flow of heat through the construction. With Type 2 migration the heat flow toward the surface opposite to the fire exposure is aided by a very significant latent heat transfer, but with the displacement of moisture the moisture moment gradually increases. Finally, with Type 3 migration a slight increase of heat flow caused by transfer of sensible heat by the moving moisture will be strongly overshadowed by the increase of moisture moment. It is seen now that migration Types 1 and 3 will definitely, and Type 2 will possibly, result in an increase of thermal fire endurance over the value calculable by the assumption of no mass migration along and opposite to the heat flow. It seems most probable, therefore, that the ease of mass transfer in these directions, and in turn the permeability of the material, is the most important factor affecting the gain in thermal fire endurance.

As Sereda and Hutcheon noted, knowledge in this field has not yet developed far enough to enable one to deal with the problem of combined heat and mass transfer in its real complexity. From calculations based on the assumption of no mass transfer perpendicular to the isothermal surfaces one can only expect to find the lower limit of the fire endurance of moisture containing building elements. It will be shown, however, that if combined with experimental results, even this information can be of considerable value.

Although learning about the thermal properties of materials in the temperature interval of interest generally represents the bulk of the work, there are other problems to solve before successfully calculating the thermal fire endurance. First, a rigorous definition of the standard fire exposure should be found which could supplement the vague definition in ASTM Method E 119.

After evaluating a large number of temperature measurements taken from the surface exposed to fire of standard fire test specimens, it was concluded that conditions met during a fire endurance test are well approximated by taking the standard fire exposure equivalent to the transfer of radiant heat to the fire-exposed side of a construction from a black surface, the temperature of which varies according to the so-called time-temperature curve of ASTM Method E 119. Nevertheless, to facilitate computer calculations, the time-temperature curve was replaced by the following analytic expression

$$T_f = 294.4 + 750[1 - \exp{(-0.06326t^{1/2})}]$$
$$+ 2.840t^{1/2}\ldots(13)$$

This is only slightly different from the so-called *CSTB* function (11), and approximates the time-temperature curve within ±6 C in the 15-min to 8-hr interval.

The laws governing the mechanism of heat flow through a building element during fire exposure are fairly well established. In the case of solid (not hollow) walls the heat flow is one dimensional, and hardly any problem arises. As mentioned, at the side exposed to fire, the heat transfer can be regarded as taking place by radiation between a black body of temperature T_f, (representing the furnace in standard fire tests) and the surface of the building element at $x = 0$, through a nonabsorbing medium. The heat flux can be calculated from the Stefan-Boltzmann law, and by combin-

ing it with the Fourier law the following boundary condition results

$$k\frac{\partial T}{\partial x} + \sigma e (T_f{}^4 - T^4) = 0 \qquad \text{at } x = 0\ldots(14)$$

Within the solid, the heat transfer takes place by conduction according to the Fourier equation

$$\frac{\partial}{\partial x}\left(k\frac{\partial T}{\partial x}\right) = \rho c\frac{\partial T}{\partial t}, \qquad \text{for } 0 < x < L\ldots(15)$$

At the surface opposite to fire exposure, the heat transfer is by combined convection-radiation mechanism to nonreflecting surroundings. The radiant heat transfer is again calculable from the Stefan-Boltzmann law. The convective transfer can be described satisfactorily by an empirical equation given by McAdams (12). A combination of these laws with the Fourier law yields the boundary condition for the unexposed surface

$$k\frac{\partial T}{\partial x} + \sigma e(T^4 - T_o{}^4) + \beta(T - T_o)^{5/4} = 0,$$
$$\text{at } x = L\ldots(16)$$

The initial condition is

$$T = T_o, \quad \text{for } 0 \le x \le L, \quad \text{when } t = 0\ldots(17)$$

In all calculations T_o was taken as 294.4 K (21.2 C), and e was selected as 0.9—a good average for the materials listed in Table 1. The fact that e decreases slightly with an increase in temperature was disregarded.[13]

In the case of hollow walls, the heat flow is, at least approximately, two-dimensional. Besides the increased labor in solving such cases, a new problem arises —the extremely complicated mechanism of heat transfer within an enclosure bounded by gray surfaces.[14] In the

---

[13] Owing to the very high temperatures the decrease of e may be significant at the exposed surface. This fact, however, has little effect on the result because the heat transfer coefficient is very high anyway, and the heat flux is controlled by the thermal resistance of the solid (13).

[14] See (12) for the definition of gray surfaces.

present series of studies Gebhart's method (10) of calculating the radiation-exchange in enclosures was utilized. The heat transferred by convection between the surface elements of the enclosure was also taken into account.

All calculations were executed on IBM 1620 and 7090 computers. The computer programs were based on a

course, not at variance with Eq 12, since τ_d is function of the properties of materials and geometry of construction.) The ψ versus τ_d plot, based on computed results, is shown in Fig. 8. Although the plot was based on information obtained for five materials of widely different characteristics and several different geometries, all points seem to lie within

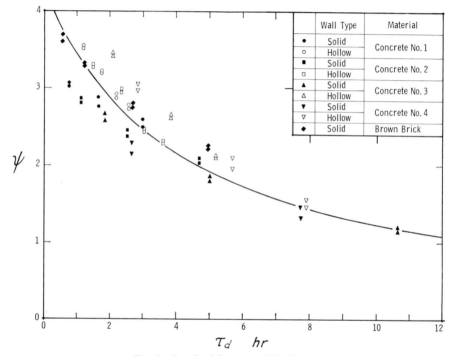

	Wall Type	Material
●	Solid	Concrete No. 1
○	Hollow	
■	Solid	Concrete No. 2
□	Hollow	
▲	Solid	Concrete No. 3
△	Hollow	
▼	Solid	Concrete No. 4
▽	Hollow	
◆	Solid	Brown Brick

FIG. 8—Result of Computer Calculations.

numerical procedure similar to that described by the author (8). The correctness of the assumed mechanisms of heat flow, presented by Eqs 13 to 17, was proved by the case of the $2\frac{1}{2}$- and 6-in. brick walls (in oven-dry condition), where the difference between the computed and experimental results was less than 5 min.

After expressing the results of computer calculations in terms of figure of merit of moisture, it was found that ψ could be correlated with τ_d with fair degree of success. (This finding is, of

a relatively narrow band. The best curve representing the mean can be given approximately by

$$\psi = \frac{4.3}{1 + 0.25\tau_d} \quad \dots\dots\dots (18)$$

This equation is expected to yield the lowest possible value of ψ at a given τ_d, and is strictly correct only for certain hypothetical materials.

As mentioned, to find the relation between ψ and τ_d, 49 fire endurance tests were carried out in the second part of the present series of investigations. All tests were performed on 32- by 32-in. specimens, using an electric furnace with 30- by 30-in. opening. The heat input was controlled to make the furnace temperature follow the standard time-temperature curve. The temperature of the unexposed surface was measured by three thermocouples placed under as-

construction all specimens were installed in a furnace and dried for 6 hr at about 105 C. The oven-dry weight of the specimens was recorded immediately after their removal from the furnace. Some were tested in oven-dry condition, others were transferred into polyethylene enclosures for storage and conditioning. Before the scheduled fire test, steam was

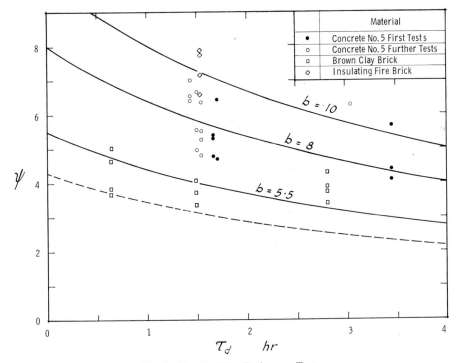

FIG. 9—Result of Fire Endurance Tests.

bestos pads along a diagonal. Although these tests could not qualify in every respect for standard fire endurance tests. experience over several years has shown that there is no significant difference in thermal fire endurance values obtained by these small-scale tests and by full-scale standard tests.

Altogether, 17 specimens were built which represented three different materials and seven different geometries (Table 1). Four to five weeks after their

introduced into the enclosure for a period necessary for the specimen to reach the desired moisture level. The actual moisture content was determined by weighing the specimen about 1 hr before the fire test.[15]

To obtain a sufficiently large number

[15] The moisture distribution in the specimens was unquestionably symmetrical; therefore, as noted in connection with Fig. 7, the distribution of moisture across the specimen was expected to have no effect on the fire endurance test results.

of experimental data, twelve of the specimens were subjected to fire test more than once. With specimens made from Concrete 5, some loss of the nonevaporable water content was experienced following the first test. No further dehydration could be detected during subsequent tests. Because the first test had undoubtedly brought about some permanent changes in the properties of concrete, once-tested concrete specimens were treated as if made from different material. The oven-dry weight of repeatedly tested specimens was taken as the weight immediately after the previous test.

The ψ versus τ_d plot based on this experimental series is given in Fig. 9. The considerable spread of the points may be understood in the light of the following observations: (1) The reproducibility of thermal fire endurance value was ±5 min, (2) The estimated accuracy of the weight measurements was ±100 g, equivalent to a moisture content of ±0.1 to ±0.3 per cent by volume, (3) Undoubtedly, there were more than negligible differences in the properties of specimens of supposedly identical materials.

In spite of the considerable spread of points, the following seem to have been proved. In practical cases ψ is always greater than the value calculable with the assumption of zero permeability in the direction of heat flow. (The ψ versus τ_d relation corresponding to this assumption is a dotted curve in Fig. 9.) As expected, ψ increases with the permeability of the material. The experimental results seem to support the assumption that the two most important variables on which ψ depends are τ_d and κ, that is

$$\psi \approx f(\tau_d, \kappa) \dots \dots \dots \dots (19)$$

Also, ψ decreases slightly with an increase in τ_d.

The spread of the points in Fig. 9 is somewhat overemphasized by the selection of the vertical scale. The total range of variation of ψ is, in fact, not too great (from 3.3 to 7.9); thus, further experiments aimed to find an explicit form of Eq 19 would serve little practical purpose. The accuracy yielded by Eq 20 will probably prove sufficient from the engineering point of view

$$\psi = \frac{b}{1 + 0.25\tau_d} \dots \dots \dots (20)$$

where b is a function of κ and can be taken as:

b = 5.5 for brick, dense concretes, and gun-applied concretes,

b = 8.0 for lightweight concretes, and

b = 10.0 for cellular concretes.

The curves representing Eq 20 with these recommended values of b are also in Fig. 9.

Discussion

The problems connected with an effort to standardize the moisture condition of fire test specimens have been discussed briefly. There are great differences in the sorption characteristics of building materials. At normal atmospheric conditions many building materials cannot hold sufficient moisture to affect the result of fire test to any appreciable degree; therefore, rigid insistence on a single standard conditioning procedure for all materials is inappropriate. On the other hand, for most concretes, the presence of moisture is only one problem, and an all-out effort to reduce the moisture content to some standard level may not give the results desired.

There is much information available (4,15) which shows that at 28 days, even under very favorable conditions, the hydration of the portland cement paste is far from being completed. It is obvious that not only the mechanical, but also the thermal properties of concrete, are strongly dependent on the degree of hydration. Thus, terminating the hydration by subjecting the test specimen to accelerated drying at an age of 28 days, The process of conditioning need no longer be regarded as equivalent to drying. On the contrary, this process can serve its true purpose: the development of the microstructure which is charac-

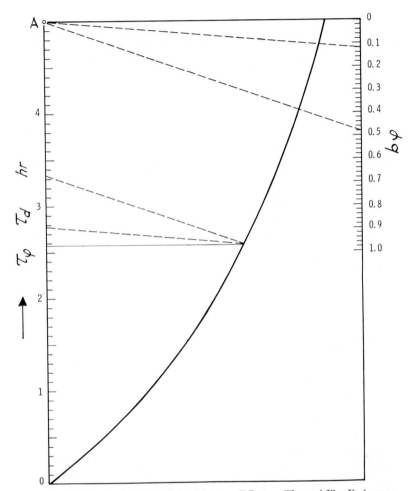

FIG. 10—Nomogram for Determining Moisture Effect on Thermal Fire Endurance.

or even earlier, may result in a material which can hardly be regarded as representative of what it would become under normal service conditions.

If the effect of moisture on the fire endurance of a construction is known, the whole problem of conditioning may be considered in a completely different light.

teristic of the material after several years' service.

Storage at moderately elevated temperatures (say 40 to 50 C) in an atmosphere of higher than 95 per cent RH for at least one month could probably be regarded as a desirable conditioning procedure for most concretes. It is known that up to about 100 C the products of hydration reactions are practically unaffected by the temperature (16,17), but the rate of the reactions is greatly increased at elevated temperatures (4). If the material is not expected to spall, after a month of curing, the specimen can be subjected to fire test at relatively high pore saturation. If the material is liable to spall, forced-drying at about 90 C may be applied for a short period to reduce the moisture to a level probably to be met under adverse service conditions.

Of course, the reduction of a fire test result to some other moisture level is possible only if the moisture content of the specimen had been accurately determined prior to the test. The average moisture content of a specimen may be measured fairly accurately by means of a recently described sampling technique (18), if a sufficient number of samples are taken from well selected locations. Further increase in the accuracy is possible by a combination of sampling and weighing the whole specimen with the aid of load cells.

The correction of a fire test result for a different moisture content has three steps: (1) calculation of τ_d from experimental values of τ_φ and φ as described below, (2) application of the experimental or calculated sorption isotherm to find the value of φ under the expected service conditions, (3) calculation of τ_φ corresponding to this latter value of φ.

Step 1 involves the solution of Eq 21, which is a result of combining Eqs 11 and 20, for τ_d

$$\tau_d^2 + \tau_d(4 + 4b\varphi - \tau_\varphi) - 4\tau_\varphi = 0 \quad . . (21)$$

where, as mentioned earlier:
$b = 5.5$ for brick, dense concrete, and gun-applied concrete,
$b = 8.0$ for lightweight concrete, and
$b = 10.0$ for cellular concrete.

Although the solution of Eq 21 presents no problem, to facilitate the calculations

a nomogram is given in Fig. 10. The same nomogram can be used to find τ_φ corresponding to a new φ value which is required in Step 3.

The use of the nomogram is illustrated by this example: A lightweight, concrete-block wall has yielded 3.33-hr fire endurance when tested at 6 per cent (by volume) moisture. Question: What is the fire endurance of the wall at 1.5 per cent moisture?

For lightweight concretes $b = 8.0$, thus $b\varphi = 0.48$ for $\varphi = 0.06$. Connect the point corresponding to this value on the right-hand side scale with Point A. A line drawn parallel to this from 3.33 on the left scale will cut the curve at 2.58 hr which is the value of τ_d. For $\varphi = 0.015$, $b\varphi = 0.12$. Again, connect this point on the right scale with Point A, and a line drawn parallel to this from the previously determined point of the curve will intersect the left scale at the value of τ_φ pertaining to 1.5 per cent moisture, 2.77 hr, in this case.

It would seem a good practice to regard, not the experimental fire endurance, but the value corresponding to the dry condition, τ_d, as the basic information. This could then be used to assign specific values to the fire endurance in specific applications. According to this concept, the wall mentioned in this example may get 3-hr fire endurance when used as an outside wall in certain regions where the average RH is high, but may be regarded only as a 2-hr wall when used as a partition in another region where the winter heating season is long.

Acknowledgment:

The author thanks S. D. Baxter, NRC Computation Centre, and his staff for preparing the computer program, and E. O. Porteous for carrying out the fire tests. This is a contribution from the Division of Building Research, National Research Council, Canada and is published with the approval of the Director of the Division.

SYMBOLS

A = constant, defined by Eq 9, dyne

b = factor, function of κ, hr

B = constant, defined by Eq 10, J/cm sec deg K

c = specific heat, J/g deg K

d = distance, explained in Fig. 7, cm

e = emissivity, dimensionless

E = modulus of elasticity, dyne/cm²

f = function

h = heat transfer coefficient, $J/cm²$ sec deg K

k = thermal conductivity, J/cm sec deg K

l = thickness of dry layer, cm

L = thickness of slab, cm

p = pressure, dyne/cm²

p_o = normal saturation pressure, dyne/cm²

q = heat flux, $J/cm²$ sec

Q = isosteric heat of adsorption, J/g

t = time, sec

T = absolute temperature, deg K

v = velocity, cm/sec

x = variable, cm

Greek Letters:

α = coefficient of linear thermal expansion, cm/cm deg K

β = constant, 0.000178 $J/cm²$ sec (deg K)$^{5/4}$

δ = fraction of vapors readsorbed, dimensionless

ϵ = effective porosity, cm³/cm³

η = viscosity, g/cm sec (poise)

κ = permeability, cm²

Λ = thickness of moisture clog, cm

ν = Poisson's ratio, dimensionless

ρ = density, without subscript: bulk density of solid (adsorbent), g/cm³

σ = Stefan-Boltzmann constant, 5.67 × 10^{-12} $J/cm²$ sec (deg K)⁴

σ_f = fracture stress, dyne/cm²

τ = thermal fire endurance, hr

φ = volume of adsorbate per unit volume of adsorbent, cm³/cm³

ψ = figure of merit of moisture, defined by Eq 11, dimensionless

Subscripts:

atm = atmospheric

av = average

c = of moisture clog

d = in dry condition

  = of the furnace; representing standard fire exposure

l = at $x = l$

o = at $x \gg L$; when $t = 0$

s = of the surface

w = of water

φ = at moisture content φ

REFERENCES

(1) T. C. Powers and T. L. Brownyard, *Proceedings*, Am. Concrete Inst., Vol. 43, 1946–1947, pp. 101, 249, 469, 549, 669, 849, 933.

(2) T. Z. Harmathy, paper in process.

(3) T. C. Powers, *Proceedings*, Fourth International Symposium on the Chemistry of Cement, Vol. 2, National Bureau of Standards, 1962, p. 577.

(4) L. E. Copeland, D. L. Kantro, and G. Verbeck, *Proceedings*, Fourth International Symposium on the Chemistry of Cement, Vol. 1, National Bureau of Standards, p. 429.

(5) L. E. Copeland and R. H. Bragg, *ASTM Bulletin 204*, Feb., 1955, p. 34.

(6) G. W. Shorter and T. Z. Harmathy, *Proceedings*, Institute of Civil Engrs., Vol. 20, 1961, p. 313.

(7) T. C. Powers, L. E. Copeland, and H. M. Mann, *Journal*, Portland Cement Assn., Research Development Laboratories, Vol. 1, No. 2, 1959, p. 38.

(8) T. Z. Harmathy, *Symposium on Fire Test Materials*, ASTM STP 301, Am. Soc. Testing Mats., 1961.

(9) T. Z. Harmathy, *Journal Applied Physics*, Vol. 35, 1964, p. 1190.

(10) O. Krischer, *Die wissenschaftlichen Grundlagen der Trocknungstechnik*, Springer-Verlag, Berlin, 1956, p. 223.

(11) J. P. Fackler, "Cahiers Centre Scientifique et Technique du Bâtiment," No. 37, Cahier 299, April, 1959.

(12) W. H. McAdams, *Heat Transmission*, Second Edition, McGraw-Hill, New York, N. Y., 1942, pp. 51, 240.

(13) T. Z. Harmathy and J. A. C. Blanchard, *Canadian Journal Chemical Engineering*, Vol. 41, 1963, p. 128.

(14) B. Gebhart, *Heat Transfer*, McGraw-Hill, New York, N.Y., 1961, p. 117.

(15) J. H. Taplin, *Australian Journal Applied Science*, Vol. 10, 1959, p. 329.

(16) F. M. Lea and C. H. Desch, *The Chemistry of Cement and Concrete*, Second Edition, E. Arnold, London, 1956, p. 187.

(17) J. D. Bernal, *Proceedings*, Third International Symposium on the Chemistry of Cement, Cement Concrete Assn., London, 1954, p. 216.

(18) T. Z. Harmathy and E. O. Porteous, *Building Note 42*, Division Building Research, National Research Council, Canada, July, 1963.

DISCUSSION

C. C. Carlson[1] and M. S. Abrams[1]— ASTM Committee E-5 has long wrestled with the problem of moisture and its proper handling with respect to fire tests and fire endurance evaluation. Some of the concepts presented in the paper may provide the answers that Committee E-5 is seeking.

The author's moisture clog concept and the formation of a moisture laden layer behind the fire exposed surface of concrete seems to provide a plausible explanation for a phenomenon we have observed in fire tests of unrestrained, pre-tensioned-prestressed beams. In such tests, where the beams were naturally dried initially to 70 per cent RH in the deepest section (as required by the standard), we have seen liquid water exuding from the ends of the twisted wire prestressing strands. The water apparently followed the small channels available between the wires. The strands had, in these instances, a minimum concrete cover of 2 in. On other occasions we witnessed liquid water being discharged under considerable pressure into the hot furnace from fine cracks and surface blemishes on the beams. It appears, however, that when a concrete specimen is dried to an equilibrium relative humidity of 70 per cent, the condensation and re-evaporation process is such that dangerous steam pressures are not likely to develop. The absence of spalling would seem to indicate that the drying of the concrete to the stated equilibrium relative humidity has produced a pore structure having the proper permeability for the resulting fractional pore saturation to prevent a moisture clog buildup. We have observed, though, that the danger of spalling due to thermal stress (thermal spalling) is present when there is heavy restraint of thermal expansion. In some instances (thin slabs within a heavy restraining frame) the spalling, if one could call it spalling, has been sufficiently violent to fail the specimen in a single occurrence.

The concept of referring actual fire test results obtained at an arbitrary moisture condition to any desired in-service condition is indeed useful. To accomplish this the author notes: (1) The φ value of the material under the expected service conditions must be determined, (2) The moisture content and properties of the material necessary for evaluating the constant b in Eq 20 for the required in-service conditions must be known to calculate the corresponding τ_φ, and (3) The actual fire test should be conducted on a specimen which has been conditioned in a manner such as to produce a microstructure within the component material which compares with that of similar material after several years of service. It appears to us that the determination of the proper microstructure of the material and the suggested method for realizing it may entail some difficulties. However, these difficulties are not

[1] Manager and senior research engineer, respectively, Fire Research Section, Research and Development Laboratories, Portland Cement Assn., Skokie, Ill.

insurmountable. The suggested procedure of storing concrete in an atmosphere at 40 to 50 C and 95+ per cent RH for 30 or more days might serve as a first approximation of the desired end for most concrete mixes and types. In some recent work done at the Portland Cement Association Laboratories, a 3 by 3 ft by 6 in. thick, normal weight concrete slab, moist cured for seven days at 73 F, followed by drying in air for 21 days at 50 per cent RH at 73 F, was subsequently exposed to air in a kiln at 85 per cent RH and 150 F (65.5 C) for 2.1 months. The latter treatment was considered productive of a moisture condition in the cooled slab which would be in equilibrium with air at 73 F and approximately 75 per cent RH. The conditioning procedure did produce a fairly uniform humidity gradient of 75 per cent through the section which compared closely with the distribution of moisture obtained in a companion slab of the same concrete naturally conditioned at 35 per cent RH and 73 F for 3.6 months. The fire endurance of the naturally dried slab was 186 min. This compares with 178 min for the slab conditioned at 85 per cent

RH and 150 F. The depression of only 8 min in the fire endurance indicates that the microstructure and moisture condition of the specimen conditioned at 85 per cent RH and 150 F was not greatly different from that of naturally dried (35 per cent RH and 73 F) concrete. Other drying methods which made use of temperatures to 200 F and a very low RH or, that even involved subsequent rewetting treatments produced depressions in the fire endurance of as much as 20 min.

In conclusion, we would like to congratulate the author for his fine contribution to the field of fire research. His approach to the problem of assessing fire resistance of constructions as they will actually be used is in strict conformity with the main purpose of ASTM Method E 119. He has shown that the formidable difficulties of determining moisture effect on the fire resistance of materials can be attacked analytically to produce very useful engineering information. Undoubtedly, other variables affecting fire resistance will also yield to analytical methods.

FIRE ENDURANCE OF SMALL GYPSUM SLABS

By J. V. RYAN, PERSONAL MEMBER, ASTM[1]

SYNOPSIS

A study was undertaken to obtain increased knowledge of the relationship between moisture content of gypsum plaster and its fire endurance. Specimens 2-ft square were prepared in nominal thicknesses of 3, $1\frac{1}{2}$, $\frac{3}{4}$, and $\frac{3}{8}$ in. They were conditioned in air at 23 C and 50 per cent relative humidity for periods ranging from 1 to 259 days. Each specimen was exposed to fire, controlled to produce the furnace time-temperature curve defined in ASTM Methods E 119. The fire endurance was taken as the elapsed time to a limiting temperature rise of 139 C on the unexposed surface.

The relationships between fire endurance and each of several factors—age, thickness, weight loss, and moisture content—are presented. It is shown that endurance did not change significantly during the initial aging period, despite appreciable change in moisture content. The initial period was followed by an intermediate period of aging marked by more significant changes in endurance. Finally there was an extended period of small changes in endurance. It was shown that endurance was affected by fairly small changes in the moisture content of gypsum plaster as equilibrium was approached.

ASTM Methods E 119[2] includes the provision:

"The material or construction shall not be tested until a large proportion of its final strength has been attained, and, if it contains moisture, until the excess has been removed to achieve an air-dry condition."

This recognizes the fact that the fire endurance of a structure is dependent on the strength and the moisture content of its elements. It further recognizes the principle that the condition of the specimen, at the time of its fire test, should be equivalent to that of the building when the hazard to life and property will be greatest—after full occupancy rather than during construction. The severity of fire resulting from burnout would also be greater after occupancy.

The fire testing of building materials and structures began about 1890 (1),[3] with each investigator following procedures of his own choice. General agreement on a procedure applicable to various building elements led to the adoption, in 1918, of the initial version of the present standard test method. That version did not recognize moisture content, since it allowed testing "as soon after construction as desired" and did not specify temperature and humidity conditions under which any aging was to be carried out. Subsequent study by the committee having jurisdiction has led to the previously quoted provision.

---

[1] Physicist, Building Research Div., National Bureau of Standards, Washington, D. C.

[2] Methods of Fire Tests of Building Construction and Materials (E 119), *1964 Book of ASTM Standards*, Part 14.

[3] The boldface numbers in parentheses refer to the list of references appended to this paper.

However, possible revisions of that section are under study as more information is developed on the relationship between fire endurance and moisture content.

Gypsum plaster was chosen because it undergoes large changes in moisture content, dries comparatively quickly, is easy to work with, and is used frequently as fire protection. It is one of a group of building materials that are supersaturated with moisture when placed in a building. In mixes of calcined gypsum, aggregate, and water to achieve a workable material, the mix water may amount to nearly half the total weight of

INVESTIGATION

Each specimen for fire test was a 2-ft-square slab of gypsum-vermiculite plaster applied to expanded metal lath attached to a furring-channel frame. The plaster was applied in layers to nominal thicknesses of 3, $1\frac{1}{2}$, $\frac{3}{4}$, or $\frac{3}{8}$ in., covering a wider range than that encountered in general practice. Each specimen was aged in an atmosphere controlled to approximately 23 C and 50 per cent RH. After aging, each was placed on top of a small gas-fired furnace and exposed to fire. The gas flow was regulated so that the average furnace temperatures approximated closely those of the stand-

TABLE 1—DATA ON MATERIALS.

Material	Net Weight, lb/bag	Density[a], lb/ft³	Net Bag Volume, ft³
Fibered gypsum plaster	101.63	48.34	2.1
Vermiculite plaster aggregate	24.39	7.26	3.3
Flat rib expanded metal lath	2.72 lb/yd²	...	...
Furring channel, ¾-in. cold rolled	0.29 lb/ft	...	...

[a] Density average of 27-ft³ each of plaster and aggregate (not compacted) bag weight average of nine bags of plaster, three bags of aggregate.

materials (2). As the plaster sets, the calcined gypsum ($CaSO_4 \cdot \frac{1}{2}H_2O$) changes to gypsum ($CaSO_4 \cdot 2H_2O$) and much of the water becomes chemically combined. The uncombined water must be removed to reach the specified moisture content. At present this is defined as that equivalent to equilibrium with air of 70 per cent relative humidity (RH) in the temperature range from 21 to 27 C, and is attained by conditioning in air at significantly lower RH.

This study was designed to determine how rapidly a typical gypsum plaster reached equilibrium moisture content in a quiescent ambient of controlled temperature and RH, and the effect on fire endurance of testing before equilibrium moisture content was reached.

ard time-temperature curve defined in ASTM Method E 119. The fire endurances of the specimens were the elapsed times to reach a temperature rise of 139 C on the unexposed surface. For approximately half the specimens this was at a thermocouple under an asbestos pad on the upper surface of the plaster; for the remainder it was at a thermocouple without pad on the upper surface of a 2-ft square piece of $\frac{1}{2}$-in. asbestos millboard laid on the furring-channel frame. The latter configuration gave an air space of $1\frac{1}{2}$ in. between the plaster and the millboard.

Materials and Specimens:

The calcined gypsum plaster, vermiculite aggregate, flat rib expanded metal lath, and furring channel were obtained through local building supply houses. The markings on bags or bundles indicated that the complete supply of each material was from a single plant. With the cooperation of the supplier and the manufacturer's representative, all bags

lath might contribute to more severe cracking of the thinnest ($\frac{3}{8}$-in.) specimens. Data on the materials are given in Table 1.

The details of the plaster base are shown in Fig. 1. The plaster mix was a

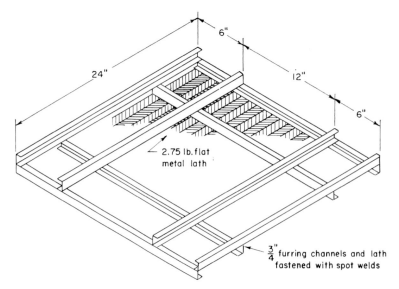

FIG. 1—Details of Plaster Base.

TABLE 2—PLASTER DATA.

| Nominal Specimen Thickness, in. | Total Batch Quantities[a] | | | Density,[b] lb/ft³ | Compressive Strength,[b] lb/in². |
	Gypsum, lb	Vermiculite, ft³	Water,[b] lb		
3	124.06	2.5	99.65	75.5	414
1½	74.44	1.5	58.67	76.4	443
¾	49.62	1.0	37.95	80.0	475
⅜	24.81	0.5	18.32	78.2	493

[a] Two 2-ft square slabs and three or nine 2-in. cubes made from each batch.
[b] Averages from four to seven batches for each thickness, three compressive strength cubes (2-in.) from each batch.

of gypsum plaster were taken from a single production lot at one plant. The lightest metal lath recommended (3) for ceilings was used to minimize the amount of metal in the specimens and its possible effect on heat transfer. Also, although experience with 1-in. thick specimens indicated satisfactory cracking behavior, it was thought that the use of heavier

nominal 1:2, that is, 1 bag of gypsum plaster to 2-ft³ of vermiculite aggregate. For this study, a bag of plaster was taken as 99.25 lb, the labeled net contents, and the plaster was batched by weight. The water was added in sufficient quantities to produce fairly consistent workabilities among the individual batches. Previous experience (2) had indicated that holding to the same amount of mix water from batch to batch could lead to appreciable variation of workability under the trowel, and of possible variation of specimen quality. Details of batching data are given in Table 2.

Two fire-test specimens, both of the same thickness, and either three or nine 2-in. cubes were prepared from each batch of plaster. The metal lath was backed with flat plastic sheets braced against the furring channel, to produce a smooth back surface rather than the usual irregular "keys" on the plaster. This was desired both to facilitate measurement of the plaster thickness and to assure satisfactory thermal contact for thermocouple junctions placed on the back of the plaster. In order to build up the thickest specimens in a single coat, it was deemed necessary to place the lath in a horizontal position and trowel the plaster on from above. This procedure was followed for all thicknesses. Two assemblies of channel, lath, and backing were placed in a dual compartment form of appropriate depth to give the desired plaster thickness. A small amount of plaster was applied and trowelled against the lath; immediately after this, the full thickness was built up. The specimens were prepared in the conditioning room. They were removed from the forms after 24 hr, the plastic backing was removed, and the specimens placed on open-shelved storage racks in the same room. They were weighed periodically during aging.

In addition to the specimens for fire exposure, specimens for measurement of moisture content versus depth were cast in metal tubing of 3 and $1\frac{1}{2}$-in. lengths. At appropriate ages, wafers were obtained by cutting out $\frac{1}{8}$-in. sections of tubing and plaster, centered on the desired depths. The plaster was removed and its moisture content determined from its weights before and after oven drying

at 55 C. Drying at this temperature does not affect water of hydration. The moisture content was taken as the weight loss divided by the oven-dried weight. These specimens were cast in tubing rather than cut from a slab because of the possibility that a coring drill might displace plaster normal to the surface, particularly while fairly fresh, leading to erroneous moisture-depth profiles.

Experimental Procedure:

When each fire endurance specimen had reached the appropriate age, its thickness was measured with a dial-gage micrometer at ten locations, and it was subjected to fire test. The furnace employed was gas-fired; it had an approximately cubical combustion chamber with a 23-in. square opening at the top. Temperatures measured by four chromel-alumel thermocouples encased in sealed iron pipes were used to determine agreement between the severity of the furnace fires and that defined by the standard test method.

The specimen was placed on top of the furnace, plaster face down, and the periphery insulated with asbestos and firebrick to minimize lateral heat flow and losses. For about half the specimens, a thermocouple was placed on the top surface of the plaster and its junction covered with a standard felted asbestos pad. For the remainder of the specimens, a sheet of $\frac{1}{2}$-in. asbestos millboard, with a thermocouple secured to its upper surface and another secured to its lower surface, was laid on top of the furring channel frame, giving $1\frac{1}{2}$-in. airspace between plaster and millboard. No asbestos pad was used over either of these thermocouples.

The fire endurance of each specimen was evaluated on the basis of the elapsed time to reach a temperature rise of 139 C above the initial value, on the unexposed surface;[4] be this the top of the plaster, under the asbestos pad, or the top of the asbestos millboard without a covering pad. However, most of the fire tests were continued well beyond this time. Temperatures were measured at 1-min intervals during the first few minutes, then at 5-min intervals up to 2 hr, and at 10-min intervals beyond 2 hr. Visual examinations of the exposed surface of each specimen were also made.

a curve faired through the data. Each curve was extrapolated back to obtain an estimate of the zero-day, or initial, weight. The data were then expressed as accumulated weight loss and are shown in Fig. 2, which indicates that the initial drying proceeded at a fairly constant rate for each thickness, and that the rates were independent of thickness. The periods of time over which the initial constant rates were effective were ap-

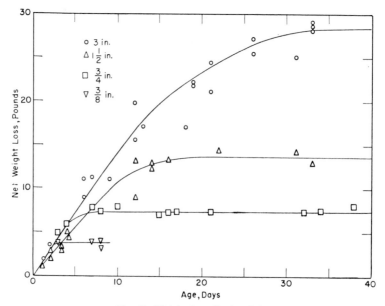

Fig. 2—Weight Loss During Aging.

Results

The actual mean thicknesses for the four groups of specimens were: 3.305, 1.639, 0.760, and 0.374 in. The standard deviations for the mean thicknesses, respectively, were: 0.058, 0.040, 0.028, and 0.028 in.

Moisture Content:

The weight of each specimen, starting at one day, was plotted against age and

proximately proportional to the thicknesses. The rates for the various thicknesses were in the range of 1.1 to 1.5 lb/ day; they persisted for only about two to three days for the $\frac{3}{8}$-in. specimens but about 15 days for the 3-in. specimens. Following the initial periods of linear drying rates, the lines in Fig. 2 show curvature to near leveling-off. The final stages indicate a very low, but observable, rate of drying. The long-time average weight losses, for specimens of the four thicknesses, expressed as per cent of initial weight of plaster (speci-

[4] This is only one of the end-point criteria applicable in fire tests of full-size specimens under ASTM Methods E 119.

men weight minus lath and furring), were in the range of 34 to 35.3 per cent.

These results appear to be in agreement with the classical description of the drying of porous solids, developed from the works of Sherwood (4), Ceaglske and Hougen (5,6) and recently reviewed by

at a constant rate. The initial linear portions of the curves in Fig. 2 are assumed to correspond to the constant-rate period. Analysis showed that the rate is independent of thickness for the plaster studied. The second, or falling-rate, period begins when the capillary

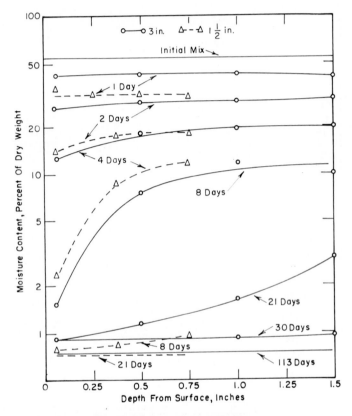

FIG. 3—Moisture Content Profiles.

Hansen and Nissan (7). Solids dry in three phases or periods, according to that description; the constant-rate period, the falling-rate period, and the final period. During the first period liquid water evaporates from the surface, much as from a body of water. Liquid from within the material is delivered to the surface by capillary action, keeping the surface wet, and drying progresses

flow rate becomes less than the rate at which surface evaporation takes place. Water then evaporates below the surface and the vapor diffuses to the surface. As the locus of evaporation (the transition between the dried surface zone and the zone of capillary flow) recedes from the surface, the rate of moisture loss is regulated by the widening dried zone which offers resistance to both the penetration of heat required for evaporation and the diffusion of the vapor to the surface. The thermal resistance increase is twofold: not only is the dry thickness greater, but the thermal

ing from about 20 days for the 3-in. specimens down to about 1 day for the $\frac{3}{8}$-in. specimens. The final drying period begins when the moisture content becomes so low that the remaining liquid

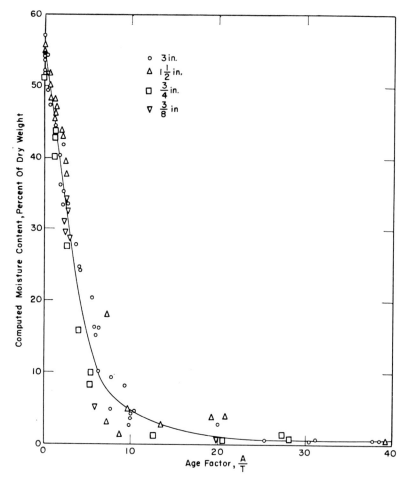

FIG. 4—Computed Moisture Content Versus Age Factor. Moisture Content Computed from Weight Loss Data for Fire Test Specimens; Age Factor Is Age Divided by Thickness.

resistance of the plaster is higher when dry than when wet. The result of the widening dried zone is a progressively falling rate of drying. The durations of the falling-rate periods, corresponding to the curved sections in Fig. 2, were different for the various thicknesses, rang-

is not sufficient for any transfer by capillary flow. It evaporates and the vapor diffuses to the surface. Because diffusion resistance and thermal resistance are at or near maxima, the drying rate is very low. Since diffusion is a concentration-gradient process, the drying rate should

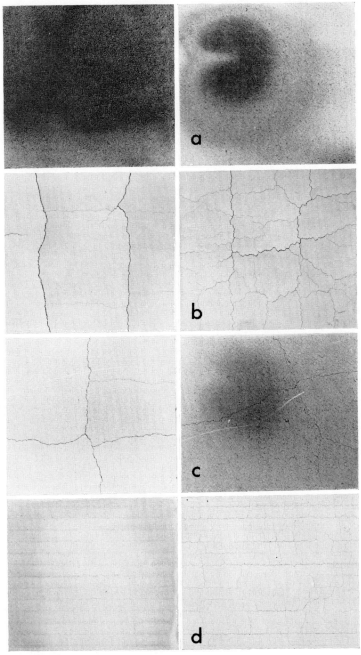

FIG. 5—Exposed Surfaces of Typical Fire Test Specimens 2-ft Square by Thickness Indicated: (a) 3-in., (b) 1½-in., (c) ¾-in., (d) ⅜-in.

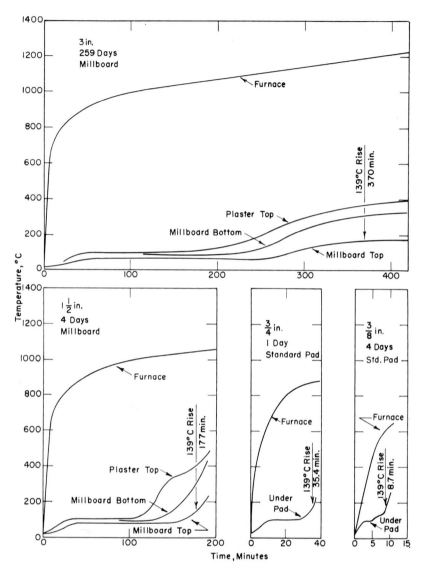

Fig. 6—Typical Time-Temperature Curves from Fire Tests.

continue to decrease, approaching zero asymptotically. The order of magnitude of the rate decrease became too small to observe in this study, and the final period data were fitted with linear end-portions of the curves.

The data obtained by oven-drying wafers from the plaster cast in metal tubing were expressed as per cent of dried

weight. They are shown as a function of age and depth in Fig. 3. The initial moisture content was computed from the batch data, decreasing the weight of mix water and increasing the weight of calcined gypsum by the amount of the former that went into hydration of the latter. Figure 3 illustrates the effects of age and thickness on moisture content and distribution. The shapes of the moisture-depth profiles are more related to moisture content than to age. For example, the 4-day profile for 1½-in. thickness is more similar to the 8-day

Moisture content data could not be obtained directly from the specimens for fire tests but values were computed from their weight loss data, allowing for the metal-lath-and-channel weight. These

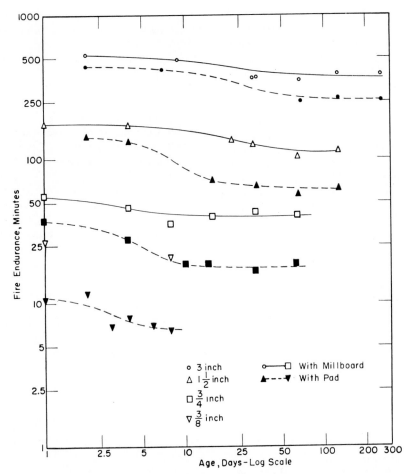

Fig. 7—Fire Endurance Versus Age.

profile for 3-in. thickness than to the 4-day profile for 3-in. The first two fall in the moisture content range of 2 to 10 per cent; the last in the range of 11 to 17 per cent. The figure does not give values for average moisture content at the different ages. These were obtained, for use in a subsequent figure, by weighting the values at the various depths.

values were plotted against an age factor (age, in days, A, divided by thickness, in inches, T), Fig. 4, to illustrate the interaction among age, thickness, and moisture content. The fact that the data for the several thicknesses may be fitted by a single curve indicates that, at least for the plaster specimens studied, moisture content and weight loss are related directly to age and inversely to thickness, for specimens and conditioning such as those in this study. A mathematical expression for the relationship was not developed. However, it might have to be in three parts, corresponding to the three periods of drying. A fit to the data for the third period, made by least-squares analysis, indicated that the weight change after age factor of 15 was only 0.5 per cent of the total weight change, or 0.2 per cent of initial weight.

Fire Endurance:

During the fire exposures, hairline craze cracking and a few continuous cracks, of not more than $\frac{1}{32}$-in. width, were observed. The crack widths increased during cooling, but each of the specimens was intact when removed from the furnace. The exposed surfaces of typical specimens (Fig. 5) show that some specimens were darkened due to partial vitrification resulting from the long exposures and high temperatures (up to $8\frac{1}{2}$ hr and 1260 C). Most of the experiments were continued beyond the time at which the 139 C surface temperature rise was observed. Typical time-temperature data plots are shown in Fig. 6.

The fire endurances were plotted against age on log scales in Fig. 7. In order to minimize the possible effect of minor thickness variations among the specimens of each nominal thickness, the endurances were first normalized, or adjusted, to the appropriate mean thickness. This was done by a power rule of the type given in *BMS 92* (8), $R_2 = R_1(T_2/T_1)^n$ where T is thickness and R is fire resistance (fire endurance is used currently, rather than fire resistance, for fire test results expressed in units of time[5]). The values of the exponent, n, used were the slopes of the

tangents, at the four mean thicknesses, to a plot of endurance versus thickness for the specimens aged the longest in each thickness group. They ranged from 0.94 for $\frac{3}{8}$-in. thick specimens to 2.94 for 3-in. thick specimens. The curves of endurance versus age (Fig. 7) indicate an initial aging period during which the endurance is reduced at a moderate rate, then an intermediate period of greater reduction, and a final period of very little reduction with age. These three periods correspond to the three periods, or phases, of drying previously described. During the phase of capillary flow to the surface (constant-rate period), the moisture content is fairly high and the endurance is relatively long. In the phase of only partly filled capillaries (the falling-rate period), the endurances drop significantly. Although the dried plaster offers increased thermal resistance, the heat capacity is greatly lowered by the reduction in water, and the net result is reduced endurance. During the final drying phase, changes in thermal conductivity and thermal capacity become small, and the fire endurances also level off.

The curves also show the effect of a layer of material, in this case asbestos millboard, behind the plaster. The effect is one of smoothing the curves but not changing their basic shape. This was expected because the asbestos millboard, of appreciable but unknown age, was not greatly susceptible to further effect of age; thus, the performance of the assembly is a function of both the changing plaster and the well-aged millboard. The ratios of the observed times with millboard to those without were greater for thinner plaster specimens, ranging from about 3:1 for $\frac{3}{8}$-in. plaster to about 1.3:1 for 3-in. plaster.

This interaction between the plaster and millboard is of interest in thinking of the results of this research in relation to

---

[5] Definition of Terms Relating to Fire Tests of Building Construction and Materials (E 176). *1964 Book of ASTM Standards*, Part 14.

actual building construction. The combination of plaster and millboard may be likened to nonsymmetrical building elements such as floors, roofs, and exterior walls. In each of these, a plaster lamina, or membrane, may be interposed between the possible fire and a horizontal, or vertical, lamina of other material. This second material in nearly all cases will have had more time to reach moisture equilibrium, will have had less initial moisture content, and will have a lower percentage of combined water than gypsum plaster. Therefore, in those cases of fires very soon after construction, the

structural integrity, even though appreciable in regard to unexposed surface temperature. Hence, the results of this study, as with any study, should be applied to particular examples of design and construction with care and reason.

The curves of Fig. 7 show the relationship between fire endurance and age for specimens of particular thicknesses. To show that the curves are specific examples of a general relationship, the ages were again converted to the same age factor (age over thickness, A/T) that was introduced in Fig. 4. As this conversion makes the age data equivalent to

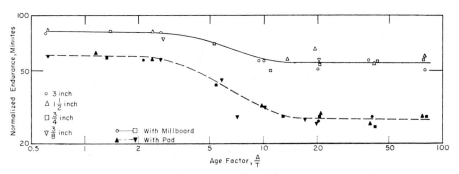

FIG. 8—Fire Endurance, Normalized to 1-in. Thickness, Versus Age Factor.

effect of age on the fire endurance will be mainly in terms of the age of the plaster.

However, the foregoing must be qualified strongly by considerations of thickness and thermal properties. This research was designed to study plaster in near isolation from other building materials. In actual buildings, the other materials—steel, concrete, wood, brick— will tend to smooth the age effect of plaster. Because they represent much greater mass and thermal capacity, proportionately, than did the millboard, they may well smooth even more effectively. However, in frequent instances, the plaster is adjacent to structural elements. Then the effect of more remote (from the fire) floor slab or external cladding may be slight in regard to

those for 1-in. thickness, the times were normalized by the power rule, to 1-in. thickness. The values of the exponent, n, were again obtained from the data for well-aged specimens; in this case average slopes between the mean thicknesses and 1.0 in. were used. They ranged from 1.03 to 1.88. The resulting values, and curves faired through them, are shown in Fig. 8. The good fit for the plotted points confirms the assumption made in analyzing the data. Therefore, the fire endurance may be expressed as the product of thickness, T, to a power and a function of age factor, A/T.

$$F.E. = T^n f(A/T).$$

The shape of the curves suggests the function, f, of age factor may be dif-

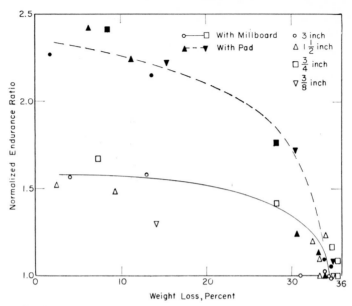

FIG. 9—Ratio of Normalized Endurance to that for Dry Plaster Versus Weight Loss (as Per Cent of Initial Weight).

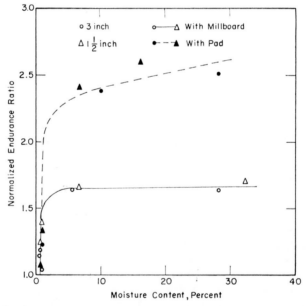

FIG. 10—Ratio of Normalized Endurance to that for Dry Plaster Versus Moisture Content.

ferent in different drying periods. The curves also show that the minimum aging, in days, for vermiculite-gypsum plaster, exposed to air on both surfaces, may be expected to be 15 to 20 times the thickness in inches.

The data were then examined with regard to the relationships between weight loss and endurance, and between endurance and moisture content. The latter was the basic aim of this study, but nondestructive measurement of moisture content presents difficulties. Therefore, the former is included as of possibly more use in the preparation of specimens for fire tests, whereas the latter is of importance in understanding the mechanisms involved in the fire endurance of plaster and similar materials. For this purpose, the relative effects on fire endurance time were deemed more generally useful than the actual times, so the data were expressed as ratios of normalized endurance to a minimum value, corresponding to dry plaster. These ratios were plotted against weight loss per cent, Fig. 9. The figure again shows the smoothing effect of the millboard topping, in that the relative time for wet plaster with millboard is 1.6 whereas that for wet plaster alone is 2.4. Figure 10 shows the same endurance ratios, relative to dry plaster, plotted against moisture content.

The curves of relative endurance against weight loss and against moisture content, Figs. 9 and 10, show that fire endurance time is very sensitive to changes in these related variables near equilibrium with the ambient. This may be understood by consideration of the heat and mass transfer phenomena involved. The temperature of the unexposed surface of a slab of gypsum plaster in a fire exposure, and the time required for a given change of that temperature, are both determined by the effective thermal properties. By the normalization carried out, thickness has been eliminated as a variable, but specific heat (c), density (ρ), thermal conductivity (k), and heat transfer coefficients (h) at both surfaces vary with moisture content. So, also, does the ease with which the moisture is transferred from within the plaster. The ρc product is made up of sensible heat absorbed by the materials, latent heat of calcination, and latent heat of evaporation. The sum of these decreases with decreasing moisture content, although latent heat of calcination increases as long as the hydration process continues. The thermal conductivity of the plaster with pores nearly filled with water is several times that of the same plaster with air-filled pores. The heat transfer at both surfaces is very greatly influenced by the mass transfer of water vapor. The mass transfer of water vapor from within the plaster is dependent on the distance to the surface, the size of the pores, and whether the pores are filled with air, water vapor, liquid water, or combinations of these.

Whatever portion of the three phases of drying has not been completed during aging will be completed during fire exposure. For plaster still in the first phase, the high thermal capacity (ρc product), high surface heat transfer, and evaporation of water at the unexposed surface all tend to retard the surface temperature rise. These are offset partially by the high thermal conductivity and the relatively short paths for heat penetration and vapor migration. However, the net effect is long fire endurance. For plaster in the second phase, the ρc product and surface transfer coefficient have dropped and water no longer evaporates at the plaster surface. They more than offset the effects of sharply reduced thermal conductivity, the net effect being moderate reduction of fire endurance. For plasters already in the third phase by the start of fire exposure, the surface transfer and thermal conductivity changes are negligible. Therefore, although changes in the ρc product are comparatively small, their effects are not counteracted by those of changing conductivity.

The effects of these variables show up in the first part of the fire exposure and affect the elapsed time during which the plaster is said to be in steam. After the fire exposure has thoroughly dried the plaster, including elimination of water of hydration, the remainder of the fire endurance is a function of the thickness of plaster, the thermal properties of which are relatively constant (2).

Conclusions

The fire endurance of gypsum plaster, due in large part to chemically combined water, is also strongly influenced by the content of free moisture. This is true even for small changes in the latter as equilibrium with the ambient is approached.

During the initial drying period (of approximately three days duration for each inch of thickness for two-surface drying) very little change in fire endurance is observed, presumably due to counteracting changes in thermal properties.

The minimum expected drying period for gypsum plaster specimens of thickness small compared to length and width, and exposed to quiescent air on the two large surfaces, should be 15 to 20 days/in. of thickness. Because fire endurance is so sensitive to changes in moisture content, the termination of aging should be based on measurements related to equilibrium with the ambient. These should be of a type that can be made periodically during aging, and should be more sensitive than weight change measurements.

The above apply strictly to conditioning in air at 23 C and 50 per cent RH, but should hold closely over an appreciable range of RH and a moderate range of temperature.

References

(1) H. Shoub, "Early History of Fire Endurance Testing in the United States," *Fire Test Methods, ASTM STP 301*, Am. Soc. Testing Mats., 1961.

(2) J. V. Ryan, "Study of Gypsum Plasters Exposed to Fire," *Journal of Research*, National Bureau of Standards, Vol. 66C, No. 4, Oct.–Dec., 1962.

(3) "Types of Metal Lath and Their Uses," *Technical Bulletin 1*, Metal Lath Assn., Feb., 1956.

(4) T. K. Sherwood, "The Air Drying of Solids," *Transactions*, American Institute of Chemical Engineers, Vol. 32, No. 2, June, 1936.

(5) N. H. Ceaglske and O. A. Hougen, "The Drying of Granular Solids," *Transactions*, American Institute of Chemical Engineers, Vol. 33, 1937, p. 283.

(6) O. A. Hougen, N. J. McCauley, and W. R. Marshall, Jr., "Limitations of Diffusion Equations in Drying," *Transactions*, American Institute of Chemical Engineers, Vol. 32, 1940, p. 183.

(7) D. Hansen and A. H. Nissan, "Analysis of Drying as a Unit Process, A Problem in Heat Transfer, Mass Transfer, and Materials Science," *Transactions*, New York Academy of Science, May, 1963.

(8) "Fire Resistance Classifications of Building Constructions," Appendix B, *Building Materials and Structures Report 92*, National Bureau of Standards, 1942.

DISCUSSION

M. S. ABRAMS[1]—What is the effect on the fire endurance of the chemically combined water, especially during the initial aging period?

J. V. RYAN (*author*)—The chemically combined water contributes greatly to fire endurance, as may be seen in the time-temperature curves of plaster or plaster-protected specimens. The long, flat portions of the curves for the 259-day aged specimen (Fig. 6) are due almost entirely to chemically combined water. The moisture content of that specimen was under 1 per cent.

During hydration, the chemically combined water increases from $\frac{1}{2}$ to two molecules per molecule of $CaSO_4$, and its contribution to fire endurance increases accordingly. After hydration is completed, for the most part within the

[1] Senior research engineer, Fire Research Laboratory, Research and Development Laboratories, Portland Cement Assn.. Skokie, Ill.

first 24 hr, the effect of the chemically combined water remains constant.

However, the increase of chemically combined water during hydration corresponds to an equal decrease in the free water. The effect of one should offset that of the other. Also, a small effect on fire endurance might be expected in terms of the heat that will be required to dissociate the chemically combined water. A small, offsetting effect would be that of loss of water by evaporation. Probably each of the last two offsetting effects, and certainly their net effect, is too small to be observed in a fire test. So, although the effect on fire endurance of chemically combined water undoubtedly increases during the period of hydration, the net effect of the total water present should be comparatively small. This study indicates that it is negligible.

EFFECT OF MOISTURE ON SURFACE FLAMMABILITY OF COATED AND UNCOATED CELLULOSIC MATERIALS*

By T. G. Lee[1]; J. J. Loftus[1]; and D. Gross, Personal Member, ASTM[1]

Synopsis

A method is described for the rapid *in situ* determination of the thermal inertia for surface heating ($k\rho c$ product) of materials using a sensitive infrared detector. Experimental measurements are given of the effect of moisture content on the thermal inertia and on the surface flammability of selected cellulosic materials conditioned to equilibrium at relative humidities ranging from 0 to 99 per cent. It is shown that (1) the thermal inertia of uncoated hardboard and fiberboard material can be represented as a linear function of its moisture content, (2) if the appropriate thermal properties are used, the flame-spread factor is inversely proportional to thermal inertia, and (3) the unbroken surface film of coated materials results in a lower ignition sensitivity than that predicted on the basis of thermal inertia.

The flame-spread index resulting from the performance of a standardized flame-spread test on a material (1,2)[2] has been shown to be composed of two multiplicative components: (1) a flame-spread factor representing the ignition sensitivity of the material, and (2) a heat evolution factor representing the maximum rate of heat generation (3). A recent study of surface flame propagation on cellulosic materials showed that, except for very thin veneers, the flame-spread factor was inversely proportional to the $k\rho c$ product, the thermal inertia for surface heating (4). Here, k, ρ, and c are the thermal conductivity, density, and heat capacity, respectively. These results appeared to support a simple concept for the spread of flame on the surfaces of

cellulosic materials exposed to thermal radiation, namely, that flame propagation consists of progressive ignition of the solid when a characteristic surface temperature is reached.

The correlation between the flame-spread factor and the $k\rho c$ product was based upon a measured value for ρ and individual values of k and c obtained from handbook sources. This paper describes a simple method for determining the thermal inertia of a material from a recording of its surface temperature history during surface irradiation. This technique was originally used for measurement of rapid changes of human skin temperature (5) and is particularly attractive for *in situ* measurements on building materials, including wood and other nonhomogeneous materials.

Because of the strong influence which moisture content has upon surface flammability, a study was made of the effect of moisture content on: (1) thermal inertia and (2) flame-spread behavior of

* The research findings reported are based on work supported, in part, by the Office of Civil Defense.

[1] Chemist, chemist, and physicist, respectively, National Bureau of Standards, Washington, D. C.

[2] The boldface numbers in parentheses refer to the list of references appended to this paper.

selected cellulosic materials. The main objective was to evaluate the overall effect of moisture content and to illustrate the importance of the thermal inertia property on surface flammability without consideration of the effects of diffusion and phase change of moisture.

THEORY

The surface temperature rise θ_s of a homogeneous, semi-infinite solid which is inert, opaque, and totally absorbing, subjected to constant irradiance I on the surface, and losing heat by Newtonian cooling at the surface is given by the relation (6)

$$\theta_s = \frac{I}{H}[1 - e^{b^2} \operatorname{erfc} b]\ldots\ldots(1)$$

where:

$$b = H\left(\frac{t}{k\rho c}\right)^{1/2}$$

erfc = complementary error function,
H = surface heat loss coefficient,
t = time, and
k, ρ, and c = thermal conductivity, density, and heat capacity, respectively.

It is assumed that heat flow is one-dimensional and that the thermal properties, which may represent effective values for moist solids, are independent of temperature.

For sufficiently short times or for low values of the heat transfer coefficient (Appendix I), an approximation to the surface temperature rise is the more common expression

$$\theta_s = 2I\left(\frac{t}{\pi k\rho c}\right)^{1/2}\ldots\ldots(2)$$

To account for specimen absorptivity less than unity, it is only necessary to prepare all surfaces in a similar manner and to consider the absorbed irradiance $I = \alpha I_0$, where α is surface absorptivity

and I_0 is incident surface irradiance. While the assumption of opacity is satisfactory for many materials, natural wood is considered partly diathermanous. It has been found, however, that blackened wood surfaces are essentially opaque.[3]

Equation 2 may be rearranged to obtain

$$k\rho c = \frac{4I^2 t}{\pi \theta_s^2}\ldots\ldots(3a)$$

It is sometimes desirable to supply incident radiation periodically in order to eliminate energy reflected directly from the irradiated surface to the detector when there is a spectral bandwidth overlap. In this case, a time factor f, representing the ratio of irradiation time to total time, must be introduced. Using this factor, a simplified expression may be written for the surface temperature rise (Appendix II) of an inert, opaque, semi-infinite solid subject to periodic application of a constant effective irradiance with no heat losses

$$k\rho c = \frac{4f^2 I^2 t}{\pi \theta_s^2}\ldots\ldots(3b)$$

Determination of $k\rho c$, the thermal inertia for surface heating, simply requires (1) a sufficiently rapid recording of the temperature rise history of a blackened surface, and (2) knowledge of the magnitude of the effective irradiance, and its application period, when appropriate. For measurement times exceeding those listed in Table 4 (Appendix I), knowledge of the surface heat loss coefficient is also required, and the value of $k\rho c$ is then obtained from Eq 1 by using the plot of $(1 - e^{b^2} \operatorname{erfc} b)$ versus b.

EXPERIMENTAL METHOD

Surface Temperature:

A noncontact radiometric technique was used successfully by Hardy et al

[3] A. F. Robertson, private communication.

(5,7) for the rapid measurement of the surface temperature of the human skin and for determination of its thermal properties. This technique involves comparison of infrared radiation from the object with that from a blackbody source of known temperature.

The experimental arrangement for measuring surface temperatures used in the present study is shown schematically

falloff to the edges of the irradiated area. An opaque shutter mounted between the lamp and the specimen was used to control exposure duration.

The radiometer used for indicating temperature changes was a commercial, infrared radiation thermometer containing a thermistor bolometer detector with high sensitivity through the spectral bandwidth of the instrument. The in-

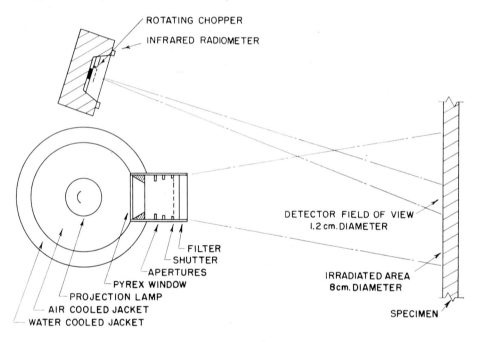

ROTATING CHOPPER
INFRARED RADIOMETER
DETECTOR FIELD OF VIEW
1.2 cm. DIAMETER
FILTER
SHUTTER
APERTURES
PYREX WINDOW
PROJECTION LAMP
AIR COOLED JACKET
WATER COOLED JACKET
IRRADIATED AREA
8 cm. DIAMETER
SPECIMEN

FIG. 1—Schematic Diagram of Apparatus for Thermal Inertia ($k\rho c$) Measurements.

in Fig. 1. The source of radiant heat was a 300-w projection lamp mounted in a ventilated housing. A line-voltage regulator and autotransformer supplied power to the lamp and permitted close control of the radiant intensity. The radiation from the lamp passed through a 2-μ, low-pass filter and impinged on a circular area, 8 cm in diameter of the specimen. The irradiation, which was typically of the order of 0.02 w/cm², was found to be uniform to within ±3 per cent on a circular area 2 cm in diameter with a gradual

strument employed germanium lens optics giving a 3-deg field of view and a spectral response from 2 to 22 μ. The system response time was 50 millisec and the sensitivity under the conditions of use was of the order of 0.1 C. The radiometer was focused on a circular area of about 1.2 cm in diameter in the center of the irradiated area where the effect of lateral heat conduction was negligibly small.

In operation, a motor-driven, reflective chopper wheel, within the radiometer, interrupted radiation from the target and reflected radiation from a controlled internal blackbody on to the detector at a rate of 90 cps. Thus, a 90-cps signal was generated whose amplitude was proportional to the difference in radiance between the target and the internal source. This signal was amplified, rectified, and recorded.

The radiometer was calibrated at the start and end of each day by substituting a large copper block with a black-coated

flected from the irradiated surface to the detector may introduce a spurious response (that is, when the spectral bandpass of the detector overlaps the wavelength region of the incident radiation), a second chopper wheel can be placed to periodically interrupt radiation incident on the specimen. Exact out-of-phase synchronization with the similarly interrupted target radiation would thus avoid the receipt of any reflected energy. A synchronous chopping arrangement of

TABLE 1—THERMAL INERTIA AND SURFACE FLAMMABILITY OF FIBERBOARD AND HARDBOARD.

Material	ρ, g/cm³	Thickness, cm	Nominal RH, per cent	Moisture Content, per cent	$k\rho c$, w² sec/(deg C)² cm⁴	$F_s{}^b$	$I_s{}^b$
Fiberboard (unpainted)....	0.27	1.19	0	0.8	2.5×10^{-4}	26.3	500
	0.27	1.20	12	3.1	3.0	21.8	403
	0.28	1.22	50	6.9	3.7	18.5	328
	0.29	1.26	76	11.2	4.5	14.8	266
	0.31	1.30	100	25.4	6.3	11.0	146
Fiberboard (painted).......	0.27	1.19	0	1.1	2.6	15.7	239
	0.27	1.20	12	3.7	3.1	13.6	191
	0.28	1.22	50	6.9	3.7	11.5	138
	0.29	1.26	76	11.2	4.5	8.82	96
	0.31	1.30	100	27.2	6.4	7.41	60
Hardboard...............	1.04	0.60	0	0.4	14	5.49	290
	1.04	0.60	12	1.9	16	4.94	244
	1.03	0.62	50	5.1	20	4.33	191
	1.02	0.65	76	9.0	24	4.05	181
	0.94	0.80	100	16.0	29	3.71	130

[a] Average for two specimens.
[b] Average for four specimens.

cylindrical cavity for the specimen. The temperature of the block was raised by means of an imbedded electrical heater and monitored by means of a precision thermometer also imbedded in the block. A series of measurements of detector output readings and copper block temperatures was made over the operating temperature range (20 to 30 C). Since the same flat black coating was used on the copper block cavity as on the test specimens, the calibration provided a means for measuring the surface temperature of the specimen.

For applications in which energy re-

this sort was employed for measuring the thermal inertia of human skin during exposure to far-infrared radiation (7).

Flame Spread:

The apparatus and experimental procedure for performing a standardized flame-spread test has been described in detail (2,3). The test requires a 6 by 18-in. specimen facing and inclined 30 deg to a vertically-mounted, gas-fired radiant panel. Ignition was initiated at the upper edge of the test specimen and observations were made of the progress of the flame front down the specimen surface, as well as the temperature rise of thermocouples in a stack supported above the specimen. The test duration was 15 min, or until sustained flame propagated down the entire 18-in. length of specimen, whichever time was less. The flame-spread index, I_s, was computed as the product of the flame-spread factor, F_s, and the heat evolution, Q

$$I_s = F_s Q \ldots \ldots \ldots \ldots (4)$$

Specimen Preparation:

Although values of thermal inertia of other types of cellulosic materials have been determined by this method, the present study on the effect of moisture was confined to cellulose fiberboard and tempered hardboard. These were chosen for the initial study to minimize the effect of the structure nonhomogeneity which is characteristic of natural woods

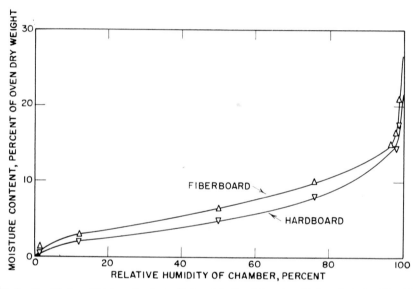

Fig. 2—Equilibrium Moisture Content of Materials Conditioned at Various Relative Humidities.

where:

$$F_s = 1 + \frac{1}{t_3} + \frac{1}{t_6 - t_3} + \frac{1}{t_9 - t_6}$$

$$+ \frac{1}{t_{12} - t_9} + \frac{1}{t_{15} - t_{12}} \ldots (5)$$

The symbols t_3 to t_{15} correspond to times in minutes from specimen exposure until arrival of the flame front at a position 3 to 15 in., respectively, along the length of the specimen. The heat evolution Q is proportional to the observed maximum temperature rise of the stack thermocouples.

Table 1 lists the thickness, density, humidity condition, and corresponding equilibrium moisture content for each specimen. The relative humidity (RH)-equilibrium moisture content relationships are shown graphically in Fig. 2.

A test specimen was prepared by applying a flat black enamel to a circular area of 7.5-cm diameter near its center. This coating was spray-applied and contained approximately 8 per cent pigment, principally carbon black, and 8 per cent nonvolatile, modified styrene vehicle. The normal paint coating, when dry, weighed 0.002 g/cm² and this produced a surface of high absorptivity (>0.94) to visible and near-infrared radiation. The 6 by 18-in. specimen was then dried in an oven at 105 C for 24 hr, allowed to cool in a desiccator, weighed, and then placed in a controlled humidity chamber to reach constant weight.

The humidity chambers (Table 2) consisted of (1) moisture-tight drums containing either calcium chloride or various

TABLE 2—METHODS USED FOR MAINTAINING VARIOUS RH CONDITIONS.

Nominal RH, per cent	Means of Achieving Humidity
0	calcium chloride ($CaCl_2$)
12	lithium chloride ($LiCl \cdot H_2O$) solution
50	commercial room air conditioner
76	sodium chloride (NaCl) solution
100	commercial humidity chamber

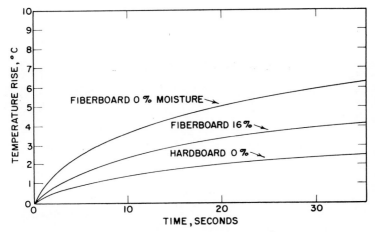

Fig. 3—Typical Surface Temperature Rise of Materials when Exposed to Effective Irradiance of of 0.018 w/cm².

saturated salt solutions (8) for maintaining a series of specified RH, (2) a commercial, room air conditioning system for maintaining 50 ± 5 per cent RH, and (3) a commercial, controlled humidity chamber especially suitable for controlling humidity in the 80 to 100 per cent RH range. The RH in all chambers was monitored by means of commercial moisture-sensitive resistance elements calibrated to ±2 per cent RH.

Specimens were transferred in polyethylene bags from their humidity chambers for weighing and thermal inertia determination. Prior to removal from the bag, the specimen was permitted to adjust to the temperature of the laboratory ambient air, when necessary. Thermal inertia determination was then made as

quickly as possible. Although the effect of variations in laboratory ambient humidity (which ranged from 35 to 50 per cent RH) was not studied, some exchange of moisture between specimen and ambient atmosphere would be expected.

After the thermal inertia determination the specimen was returned to its controlled humidity chamber for reconditioning prior to a flame-spread test. Additional specimens were conditioned and tested for surface flammability only to provide sufficient flame-spread replication data.

Results and Discussion

Figure 3 illustrates typical surface temperature-time records for fiberboard and tempered hardboard of various moisture contents. When plotted as a function of $\sqrt{t}$ (Fig. 4) the data appear as straight lines, and the initial slopes may be used to calculate values of $k\rho c$ using Eq 3a.

For times exceeding those listed in Table 4, Eq 1 was used to evaluate $k\rho c$.

For typical values of $T_s = 300$ K, $T_a = 296$ K, and $h = 1.8 \times 10^{-4}$ w/cm² deg K (for laminar conditions on a vertical plane surface with a small irradiated area), the value for H is 8.4×10^{-4} w/cm² deg K.

Because of uncertainties associated

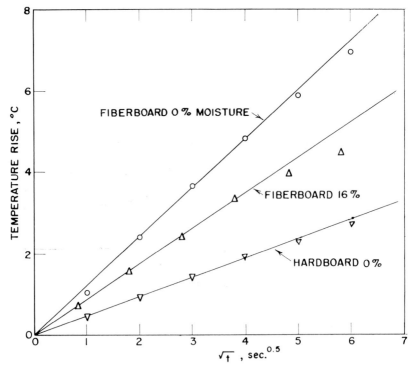

Fig. 4—Typical Surface Temperature Rise as Function of $\sqrt{t}$ for Materials when Exposed to Effective Irradiance of 0.018 w/cm².

The surface-heat transfer coefficient was calculated from

$$H = \frac{\sigma\epsilon(T_s^4 - T_a^4) + h(T_s - T_a)}{T_s - T_a} \quad \ldots (6)$$

where:
T_s = surface temperature, deg K
T_a = ambient temperature, deg K
σ = Stefan-Boltzmann constant, 5.67 $\times 10^{-12}$ w/cm² (deg K)⁴,
ϵ = surface emissivity, assumed equal to 1, and
h = convective cooling coefficient.

with surface emissivity, absorptivity, and diathermancy, all specimens for thermal inertia determination were painted with a flat black enamel which provided a uniformly high absorptivity and opacity. However, the actual value of the absorptivity is not necessary since a measurement was made of the effective or absorbed, rather than incident, irradiance using selected specimens of known thermal properties. The calculation of the effective I was based upon temperature-time records and independently deter-

TABLE 3—EFFECTIVE IRRADIANCE MEASUREMENTS.

Material	Density, ρ, g/cm^3	Thermal[a] Conductivity, k, w/cm deg C	Heat Capacity, c, w sec/g deg C	Thermal Inertia, $k\rho c$, w^2 sec/(deg C)^2 cm^4	Effective Irradiance, I, w/cm^2
Rubber	0.97	15.2 × 10^{-4}	1.77	26 × 10^{-4}	0.020
Insulating board, dry	0.23	5.03	1.21	1.4	0.019
Rigid polyvinyl chloride	1.4	12.5	0.84	15	0.018
Asbestos board	0.67	12.3	0.84	6.9	0.016
Gypsum-vermiculite plaster	0.63	18.9	1.02	12	0.015

[a] Based on measurement in guarded hot-plate apparatus (ASTM Method C 177) at mean temperature of 23 C.

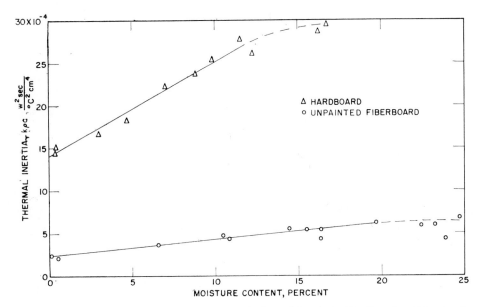

Fig. 5—Effect of Moisture Content on Computed Thermal Inertia for Hardboard and Unpainted Fiberboard.

mined values of k, ρ, and c on a variety of materials, using Eq 1. Results of these measurements are given in Table 3. All subsequent computations of $k\rho c$ were based on the average effective I value of 0.018 w/cm^2.

Linear relations between moisture content and the computed values of $k\rho c$ based on the present method for fiberboard and hardboard are indicated by the data in Fig. 5. The dotted portion of the line shows some deviation from linearity. Natural woods of intermediate densities would be expected to have values of $k\rho c$ between the two curves. The linear relationship as well as numerical values are in agreement with the findings of a previous survey of available data based on individual measurements of k, ρ, and c (9).

The computed $k\rho c$ values take into account changes in each property due to moisture. Whereas heat capacity and thermal conductivity both increase with increasing moisture content, the swelling of common woods due to moisture results

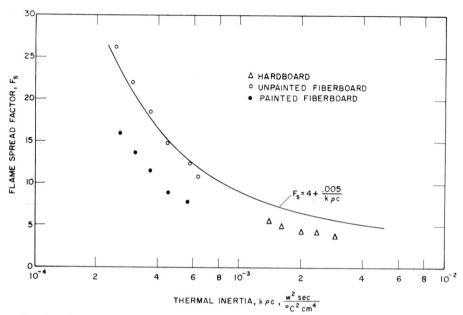

FIG. 6—Effect of Computed Thermal Inertia on Flame-Spread Factor for Materials Conditioned and Tested at Various Moisture Contents. (Curve represents data from (**4**) for other cellulosic materials.)

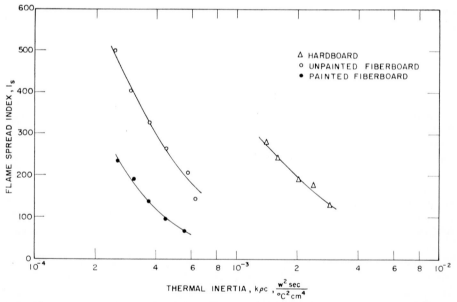

FIG. 7—Effect of Computed Thermal Inertia on Flame-Spread Index for Materials Conditioned and Tested at Various Moisture Contents.

in a decrease in density. This was particularly noticeable for hardboard at high moisture contents (Table 1).

Note that the presence of a thin, factory-applied, white paint coating on the thermal insulation fiberboard (conforming to Federal Specification LLL-I-535, Class D) had no appreciable effect on the computed values of $k\rho c$.

The measured flame-spread factors for hardboard and for painted and unpainted fiberboard are given in Fig. 6 as a function of the corresponding thermal inertia values. The flame-spread factor is seen to be inversely proportional to thermal inertia. The plotted data include measurements over the entire range of moisture content.

A relationship of this type agrees with the concept that a characteristic surface temperature must be reached prior to ignition. A high $k\rho c$ value, for example, would delay the attainment of the characteristic temperature and thus lower the flame-spread factor. In a previous study (4), flame-spread factors for a wide variety of thick cellulosic materials conditioned to equilibrium at 50 per cent RH only, were also found to be inversely proportional to the $k\rho c$ values. However, the thermal conductivity and heat capacity values used were dry values obtained from handbook sources and were not adjusted for the appropriate moisture contents. When this adjustment is made, the previous data can be represented by

$$F_s = 4 + \frac{0.005}{k\rho c} \quad \ldots\ldots\ldots\ldots (7)$$

shown in Fig. 6 for comparison. Although the flame-spread factors for hardboards appear to deviate somewhat from Eq 7, they are actually within the data scattering on which the equation was based.

The flame-spread factors for painted fiberboard were significantly different from the mean values represented by

Eq 7, even when the appropriate $k\rho c$ values were used. For flame propagation on surface-coated cellulosic materials, therefore, it appears that a higher surface temperature had to be attained in order to permit heat penetration and rupture of the coating (approximately 0.002-cm thick) and subsequent release of combustible vapors.

Figure 7 shows the measured flame-spread index, $I_s = F_s Q$, as a function of the corresponding computed values of thermal inertia for the three types of materials with various moisture contents. Since the heat release rate Q depends on the thickness as well as the density of

TABLE 4—ERROR INTRODUCED BY USING THE APPROXIMATION FOR VARIOUS ($k\rho c$) VALUES AND MAXIMUM MEASUREMENT TIMES.

Thermal Inertia, $k\rho c$, w^2 sec/(deg C)^2 cm^4	1 per cent ($b = 0.011$), sec	5 per cent ($b = 0.056$), sec	10 per cent ($b = 0.111$), sec
175×10^{-6}...	0.03	0.78	3.1
700×10^{-6}...	0.12	3.1	12
1750×10^{-6}...	0.3	7.8	31
7000×10^{-6}...	1.2	31	120

the cellulosic specimens, a single continuous function is not expected to cover both hardboard and fiberboard, which do not have comparable density or thickness. But, for a given type of specimen, the correlation between I_s and $k\rho c$ appears to be reasonable. Accordingly, the effect of moisture on the flame-spread index may be interpreted in terms of the thermal properties of the materials.

The principal sources of error involved in the $k\rho c$ determinations for this study were:

(1) The uncertainties in measurements of surface temperature rise and effective irradiance,

(2) The modification of surface conditions by application of a flat black enamel, and

(3) The use of the approximate Eq 2

at long measurement times (or high values of the heat transfer coefficient).

The coefficient of variation of the kpc computations was approximately 3 per cent based on 15 sets of duplicate determinations. The overall uncertainty in kpc due to random and systematic errors is estimated to be about ± 10 per cent. A significant reduction of this uncertainty should be possible by more precise measurement of the effective irradiance and by the use of the exact equation in place of the approximate one. The coefficient of variation of the flame-spread factor computations was approximately 4 per cent, based on 15 sets of four repeat determinations.

Conclusions

Since the movement of hygroscopic moisture and the conduction of heat are basically diffusion processes, no abrupt difference in flame-spread behavior was expected with variations in the moisture content of typical combustible materials. The results did, in fact, indicate that the ignition sensitivity, or flame-spread factor, varied in a manner closely approximating previous data—for thick cellulosic materials conditioned at a single RH—when the effect of moisture on the appropriate thermal properties was taken into account.

The radiometric method described for the direct and rapid *in situ* determination of the thermal inertia for surface heating (kpc product), is particularly attractive for building materials, including wood and other nonhomogeneous materials. Although simple measurements are conveniently made at ordinary temperatures, the method may be readily applied to measurements at much higher temperatures. The application of the method to the rapid noncontact measurement of moisture content of materials also appears feasible. Finally, consideration could be given to the use of the method for applications involving composite materials with a thin surface veneer, for which the appropriate temperature-rise relationship (10) should be employed.

Appendix I

The error in using the approximation $2b/\sqrt{\pi} = (1 - e^{b^2} \operatorname{erfc} b)$ will be within 1, 5, and 10 per cent for values of $b = 0.011$, 0.056, and 0.111, respectively. For a range in thermal inertia values, and assuming a room temperature value for H (the effective heat loss coefficient for radiation and convection) of 0.00084 w/cm² deg C, these correspond to the maximum measurement times listed in Table 4.

For very good insulating materials (low thermal inertia) increased accuracy may be achieved by continuing temperature-time observation for an extended period. A plot of temperature rise versus $1/\sqrt{t}$ becomes linear for long times and the value of kpc may be determined from the slope of the line, $\dfrac{I}{H^2} (kpc/\pi)^{1/2}$, and the intercept, I/H.

Appendix II

The surface temperature rise of a semi-infinite solid subjected to a pulsed surface flux of rectangular wave form is equal to the sum of a periodic part superposed on the rising temperature due to the average surface flux fI. The value of the transient part is

$$\theta_t = 2fI \left(\frac{t}{\pi kpc} \right)^{1/2} \dots\dots\dots (8)$$

and the periodic part at time bT, after the beginning of a heating period (11),

$$\theta_p = 2fI \left(\frac{T}{\pi kpc} \right)^{1/2} \left[(1 - f) - \frac{\phi(f, b)}{\sqrt{\pi b}} \right] \dots (9)$$

where T is the total time per cycle. The ratio of the periodic to the transient parts is

$$\frac{\theta_p}{\theta_t} = \left[(1 - f) - \frac{\phi(f,b)}{\sqrt{\pi b}} \right] \left(\frac{T}{t} \right)^{1/2} \quad \ldots \ldots (10)$$

For $f = 0.5$, the average half-cycle value of the term in brackets is less than 0.24, so

that for a chopping frequency of 90-cps ($T = 0.011$ sec), the effect becomes small (<5 per cent) for times greater than 0.25 sec.

References

(1) Interim Federal Standard 00136b (COM-NBS), Dec. 26, 1962. Available from General Services Administration Regional Offices.

(2) A. F. Robertson, D. Gross, and J. J. Loftus, "A Method for Measuring Surface Flammability of Materials Using a Radiant Energy Source," *Proceedings*, Am. Soc. Testing Mats., Vol. 56, 1956, pp. 1437–1453.

(3) A. F. Robertson, "Surface Flammability Measurements by the Radiant-Panel Method," *Fire Test Methods, ASTM STP 344*, Am. Soc. Testing Mats., 1962, pp. 33–46.

(4) D. Gross and J. J. Loftus, "Surface Flame Propagation on Cellulosic Materials Exposed to Thermal Radiation," *National Bureau of Standards Journal of Research*, Vol. 67C, Sept., 1963, pp. 251–258.

(5) J. D. Hardy and I. Jacobs, "Method for the Rapid Measurement of Skin Temperature During Exposure to Intense Thermal Radiation," *Journal Applied Physiology*, Vol. 5, March, 1953, pp. 559–566.

(6) D. I. Lawson, L. L. Fox, and C. T. Webster, "The Heating of Panels by Flue

Pipes," *Fire Research Special Report 1*, Department of Scientific and Industrial Research and Fire Offices' Committee, London, 1952.

(7) E. Hendler, R. Crosbie, and J. D. Hardy, "Measurement of Heating of the Skin During Exposure to Infrared Radiation," *Journal Applied Physiology*, Vol. 12, 1958, pp. 177–185.

(8) A. Wexler and S. Hasegawa, "Relative Humidity-Temperature Relationships of Some Saturated Salt Solutions in the Temperature Range 0 to 50 C," *National Bureau of Standards Journal of Research*, Vol. 53, July, 1954, pp. 19–26.

(9) H. B. Nottage, "Thermal Properties of Building Materials Used in Heat Flow Calculations," *Transactions*, American Society of Heating and Ventilating Engineers, Vol. 53, 1947, pp. 215–243.

(10) M. V. Griffith and G. K. Horton, "The Transient Flow of Heat Through a Two-Layer Wall," *Proceedings*, Physical Society, Vol. 58, 1946, pp. 481–487, 776.

(11) J. C. Jaeger, "Pulsed Surface Heating of a Semi-Infinite Solid," *Quarterly Applied Mathematics*, Vol. 11, 1953, pp. 132–137.